HANDS-ON MATH

◆◆◆◆◆◆◆◆◆◆◆◆◆◆

Manipulative Activities
for the K–1 Classroom

◆◆◆◆◆◆◆◆◆◆◆◆◆◆

Written by Virginia Johnson

Edited by Janet Bruno ◆ Illustrated by Terri Sopp Rae ◆ Project Director Sue Lewis
Contributions by Mary Kurth

Table of Contents

Chapter 1

Implementing Hands-On Math

Implementing Hands-On Math

Hands-On Math is a resource book of manipulative math activities designed to supplement any K–1 math program. It is built on the premise that young children learn math concepts best through hands-on experiences with concrete objects. As you implement the activities, you will see how using manipulatives actively involves students in the learning process and gives them a wonderful sense of discovery and empowerment as they explore mathematical concepts.

The core of the book consists of 15 chapters, each of which focuses on a math concept such as shapes, patterns, counting, or measurement. The time spent on a given chapter will vary according to the needs of your class.

The following chapter components provide you with a wealth of ideas for integrating manipulative activities into your math program:

✎ Bulletin Board

Most bulletin board ideas are interactive and activity-oriented in keeping with the basic premise of the book. Others are designed to feature students' work.

✎ Skills List

The skills covered in each chapter are listed so you can easily integrate these activities into your current math program. The list also provides a handy reference for assessment purposes.

✎ Learning Center

Suggestions are given for creating an independent learning center for each major concept. There are lists of specific materials and activities appropriate for center use.

✎ Chapter Activities

Typically, a chapter contains 9 to 14 hands-on activities presented in order of difficulty. Some are recommended for the whole group, while others work best in small group situations or at a learning center. For each activity, there is a complete list of the materials needed, as well as easy-to-follow directions. All of the activities can be adapted to the needs of your students.

It is important to note that the chapter activities are designed to lead children step by step from working with concrete objects to constructing pictorial representations of objects, and finally to using symbols such as numerals. For example, in students' first experiences with addition, they should combine sets of real objects, such as 3 crayons and 2 crayons. The next step is to record these experiences with pictures ( ). Finally, they describe the operation using symbols (3 + 2 = 5). In all cases, students will need guidance from the teacher connecting the manipulative activities and games with abstract symbols.

✎ Parent Letters

In Chapter 17 there is a parent letter for each concept covered. These letters strengthen the home-school connection by involving parents in their children's education. Each letter outlines a few activities that parent and child can do together to reinforce work done in class. The letters can be personalized to meet the needs of your students.

✎ Reproducibles

For your convenience, black-line masters are provided for some activities. These reproducibles are grouped together in Chapter 18.

✎ Related Literature

The topic-related literature lists in Chapter 19 can be used to integrate math with literature.

Using Manipulatives in the Classroom

In an activity-based math program, it is the teacher who holds the key to success. If you believe that manipulatives offer an innovative and effective approach to teaching math, that belief will translate into meaningful learning experiences for your students. If you have fun with manipulatives, your class will too.

There are various ways to integrate manipulative activities into your math program. Some activities are appropriate for the whole class, while others may be better suited to small groups. Or, you may introduce some activities to the whole group before placing them at a learning center for independent use.

Work stations are another alternative. Stations can be set up around the classroom, with one activity at each station. For example, when studying shapes, set up five stations where children can do shape rubbings, use pattern block shapes, make cut-and-paste shape pictures, form shapes on geoboards, and play a shape matching game. Students could rotate to all of the stations in one day, or they could visit a different station each day.

Tips on Classroom Management

An activity-based program requires more materials and promotes more movement and verbal interaction than a program using worksheets or math texts. For those of you who are ready to make manipulatives the focus of your math program, here are some management tips that will help:

▲ Allow children plenty of time to informally "play" with the manipulatives before using them in directed lessons so that later on they will be able to focus on mathematical concepts rather than on the manipulatives themselves. The amount of time set aside for exploration will depend upon the needs of your students. You will find, however, that as children develop intellectually and reach new levels of understanding they will benefit from repeated free exploration opportunities throughout the year.

▲ Introduce math manipulatives gradually. Discuss and model the safe and responsible use of these materials. It is also a good idea to rotate the materials and activities offered at any one time.

▲ Find a place to store the manipulatives so they are easily accessible to the children. Label shelves, drawers, and cabinets with words, codes, and/or pictures so students can take responsibility for cleaning up.

▲ Establish ground rules for math activity time, display them prominently, and have students role-play the rules. Enforce these rules consistently, and praise responsible behavior.

▲ Model each activity with the whole class or a small group before asking students to do the activity independently.

Rules
1. Stop and listen when you hear the signal
2. Share materials
3. Put materials back in the right spot

Collecting Materials

The materials in **Hands-On Math** are a combination of inexpensive, everyday objects and commonly available commercial math manipulatives, such as pattern blocks and Unifix® Cubes. As you read over the following lists of recommended materials, do not feel that you need to collect each and every item. Feel free to substitute materials available to you for those listed.

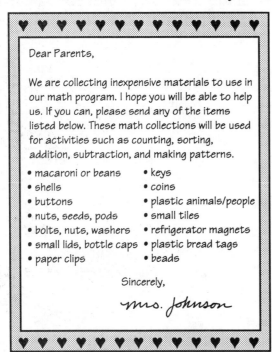

Dear Parents,

We are collecting inexpensive materials to use in our math program. I hope you will be able to help us. If you can, please send any of the items listed below. These math collections will be used for activities such as counting, sorting, addition, subtraction, and making patterns.

- macaroni or beans
- shells
- buttons
- nuts, seeds, pods
- bolts, nuts, washers
- small lids, bottle caps
- paper clips
- keys
- coins
- plastic animals/people
- small tiles
- refrigerator magnets
- plastic bread tags
- beads

Sincerely,

Mrs. Johnson

Start by enlisting the help of students and parents in collecting inexpensive materials. (There are many suggestions for the use of these "math collections" in the following chapters.) At the beginning of the year, send a letter home listing items you would like to collect. As the manipulatives arrive, place them all in a large container. Later, have students sort the materials into separate containers, then label the containers and place them in a well-marked, central location.

There are also many excellent commercial products available. Although they can be expensive, the cost of these materials can be defrayed in a number of ways:

✓ Ask your principal to allow funds earmarked for the purchase of workbooks to be used for the purchase of manipulatives instead.

✓ Write a proposal to the parent support group at your school asking for money or materials.

✓ Have a class fund-raising project, such as a garage sale or bake sale.

✓ As a learning center or a free-time activity, have the children in your class make some of the simpler manipulatives.

✓ Host an after-school or evening workshop for teachers, parents, and other volunteers. Ask participants to bring materials and spend a couple of hours making manipulatives.

✓ In lieu of a gift exchange at holiday time, have each child present the classroom with a gift chosen from the list of needed materials.

Materials for class math collections:

- macaroni in various shapes
- dry beans (pinto, navy, lima, black)
- beads of all kinds
- shells
- buttons
- nuts, seeds, rocks, stones, small pine cones, pods
- bolts, nuts, washers
- small lids, bottle caps
- plastic bread tags
- paper clips
- keys
- coins
- plastic animals/people
- small tiles
- golf tees
- spools
- refrigerator magnets

Other common materials:

- small boxes for storing math collections
- egg cartons for graphing and sorting
- plastic food containers
- food coloring to color macaroni
- toothpicks
- craft sticks
- clothespins
- old magazines and catalogs
- containers for sorting (aluminum, Styrofoam, or microwave trays; pie plates; paper plates)
- old hula hoops for concrete Venn diagrams
- tens cups (nut, soufflé, medicine, or portion cups)
- old measuring cups and spoons

Commercial products available:

- pattern blocks
- attribute blocks
- Cuisenaire® Rods
- Base Ten Blocks
- Unifix® Cubes or Multilink® Cubes
- tangrams
- plastic counters
- dice
- spinners
- geoboards
- play money
- demonstration clock
- balance scale
- kitchen scale
- thermometer
- 100s board
- timers (kitchen, egg)
- 2-cm cubes
- wooden stringing beads
- floor graph
- magnetic board
- magnetic shapes, numbers
- rubber stamps and stamp pads
- dominos
- rulers, yardstick

Chapter 2

Calendar

Calendar

The calendar activities in this chapter give students informal experiences with a wide variety of important math concepts. You can introduce the activities gradually throughout the year as your students display readiness for the concepts covered. Model each activity several times, then let the children take over the calendar responsibilities. When the activities are used with the whole class on a daily basis, students receive the necessary repetition and support for skill acquisition. The last activity, making a personal take-home calendar, encourages students to use the calendar for authentic purposes.

Skills

- Introduce time and duration
- Sequence days and months
- Identify patterns
- Practice counting (by ones, twos, fives, tens)
- Introduce place value (ones, tens, hundreds)
- Make a graph

Calendar Center and Bulletin Board

The calendar is an interactive bulletin board that is used every day, starting the first day of school. Position the calendar so that the whole class can gather round, and place it low enough so that students can easily reach the various components. Personalize the board with student artwork and seasonal decorations. Pages 14–18 describe in detail how to make and use each element at the calendar center.

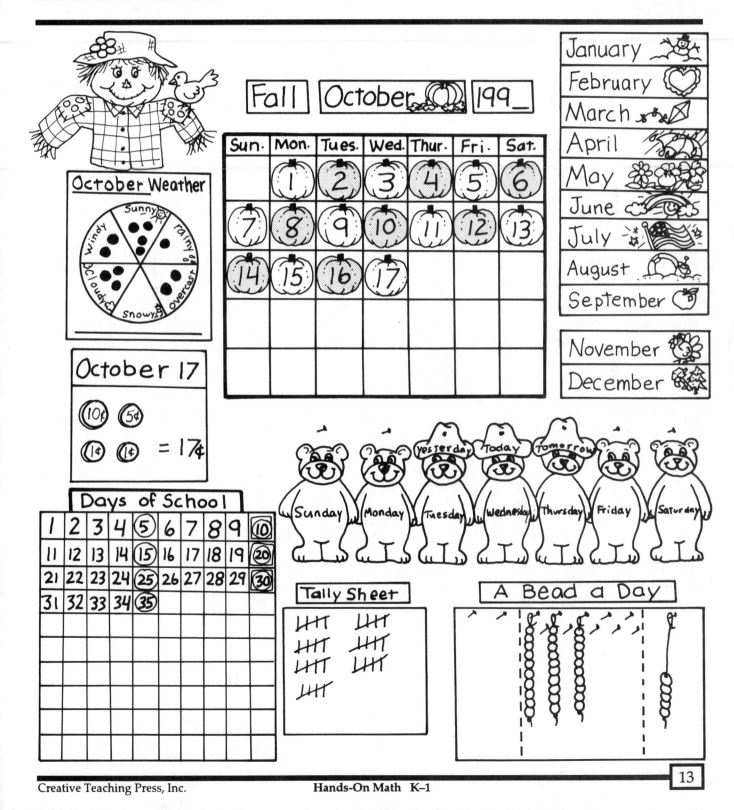

Activities

Months of the Year

Materials
- Month Cards
  (pages 152–154)
- label cards (for seasons
  and year)
- calendar cutouts
- marker

✎ Teacher Preparation

Color, cut out, and laminate the reproducible Month Cards. Make label cards for each season and for the year. Vary the cutouts to make a pattern. (For example, red and green apples or big and little pumpkins.) Write dates on the calendar cutouts. Place all of these on the calendar bulletin board as shown on page 13.

✎ Activity

The calendar helper places the new day on the calendar, states the complete date, and tells the season: "Today is Thursday, October 8, 1993. The season is fall." Then the class recites all the months in order as the helper points to the month name cards. Also have the class describe the pattern of the calendar cutouts ("red apple, green apple, red apple . . .").

Today Is . . .

Materials
- 7 Bears (page 155)
- 3 Hats (page 155)
- marker
- scissors

✎ Teacher Preparation

Reproduce and cut out seven copies of the Bear Shape. Write one day of the week on each bear. Reproduce and cut out three hats. Label each hat as shown and punch a hole where indicated. It's a good idea to laminate these. Post as shown on page 13.

✎ Activity

Each day a student moves the hats to the correct day and verbalizes the sequence shown. For example, "Yesterday was Monday. Today is Tuesday. Tomorrow will be Wednesday." The rest of the class can chant along. You can also reinforce the sequence of the days of the week by reading one of the many picture books that illustrate this concept. (See book list on page 212.)

Days of School Chart

Materials
- 100s grid (1" or 2" squares)
- fine-tipped markers in black, red, green, orange
- label card ("Days of School")

✎ **Teacher Preparation**

Attach a 100s grid to the calendar wall where the children can easily reach it. This will be used to record the days of school. After the one hundredth day of school, you will need to add a second grid.

✎ **Activity**

Every day a student records the next number in counting sequence in the next empty box on the grid. After 20 days have passed, or when you are discussing counting by fives and tens, begin marking the numbers on the chart in the following fashion:

- When counting by twos, underline the number with an orange marker.
- Circle multiples of five with the red marker.
- Put a green square around the number when counting by tens. (Every multiple of ten will have both a circle and a square around it.)

Tally the Days

Materials
- 8½" x 11" tally sheet
- fine-tipped marker, any color
- label card ("Tally Sheet")

✎ **Teacher Preparation**

Attach a plain piece of paper to the calendar bulletin board, and post the Tally Sheet label. This tally sheet will provide an additional visual record of the days of school.

✎ **Activity**

Each day, a student makes one mark on the tally sheet. Every fifth day is recorded with a diagonal line. The class counts the tallies, first by fives and then by "counting on" the leftover tallies. For example, if it is the thirteenth day of school, count like this: "Five, ten, eleven, twelve, thirteen. This is the thirteenth day of school."

A Bead a Day

Materials

- beads (one for each day of the school year)
- 20 pieces of string/yarn, long enough to hold 10 beads and be knotted (or use shoelaces)
- label card ("A Bead a Day")
- glue or tape
- tacks

✎ Teacher Preparation

Wrap one end of each string with tape, or dip the end in glue and shape into a point, so the beads will go onto the string without great difficulty. Pin the string on the calendar board with a tack so that it can be easily removed each morning to add a bead.

✎ Activity

Each day, a student adds one bead to the string. When ten beads are on the string, the teacher knots it and firmly secures it to the middle section of the board. When this section holds ten strings of ten beads, the strings are transferred to the section on the left. (These sections represent the ones, tens, and hundreds columns, but you can decide if you want to use those terms.)

After each bead is added, have students count the beads, first counting by tens, then "counting on" for the beads in the ones section. For example, if it is the thirty-fifth day of school, the counting will go like this: "Ten, twenty, thirty, thirty-one, thirty-two, thirty-three, thirty-four, thirty-five. There are thirty-five beads. That means that there have been thirty-five days of school so far."

Adding Up the Days

Materials

- magnetic play money
- magnetic board

✎ Teacher Preparation

You can purchase magnetic play money, or make your own by gluing magnet strips onto cardboard coins. As an alternative, glue Velcro® strips on cardboard coins and use them on a flannelboard.

✎ Activity

Each day, students represent the day's date with the coins. For example, for October 12, one child might use 2 nickels and 2 pennies, another might use a dime and 2 pennies, and a third might choose 12 pennies. To give practice with larger amounts of money, have students use the coins to make the number of the school day (68 cents for the 68th day of school).

Daily Schedule

Materials
- Daily Schedule Clocks (page 157)
- marker

✎ Teacher Preparation

Prepare one clock face for each regularly scheduled activity, such as math, daily news, lunch, recess, sharing, and language. Label the activity, write the time, and draw hands on the clock. You can also make a clock for special activities such as Computer Lab at 11:30 on Wednesday. Display the clocks above the calendar bulletin board (or near the class wall clock).

✎ Activity

Look at the clocks every morning and review the day's schedule. Point out the time of any special activities. Ask students to tell you the times for different daily activities. They can also reproduce the time on a demonstration clock. Throughout the day, encourage them to compare the activity clocks with the real clock.

Weather Graph

Materials
- 10 Weather Graphs (page 156)
- 1" round stickers (or a marking pen)

✎ Teacher Preparation
Reproduce one graph for each month of school, and label each with the name of a month. Attach the appropriate graph to the calendar wall.

✎ Activity
Establish with the class definitions for the weather terms on the chart. For example, "cloudy" means that clouds are visible in the sky, while "overcast" means a general cloud cover. Each morning, ask the class what the weather is like. Then ask a student to put a dot sticker or a mark (if using the marker) in the appropriate section of the graph. Display all of the completed weather graphs in the classroom so students can compare weather patterns from season to season and throughout the year.

Personal Calendar

Materials
- Calendar (page 158), 1 per student
- pencils
- 12" x 18" construction paper, 1 per student
- crayons/markers
- glue sticks

✎ Teacher Preparation
Before reproducing copies of the student calendar, you may want to fill in some of the information on the master copy.

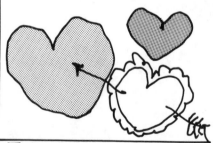

✎ Activity
Give each student a copy of the blank calendar. Model how to fill in the month, the year, and the dates. It's also fun to indicate special holidays or events. Students can glue the calendar on construction paper and decorate it with seasonal illustrations. Let them take the calendar home to use for scheduling personal activities.

Chapter 3

Geometric Shapes

3 Geometric Shapes

Most familiar objects in a child's environment can be described in terms of geometric shapes. Recognizing and labeling shapes is an important skill, but children also need experience handling, exploring, and using shapes. The following activities provide students with a variety of opportunities to "experience" shapes.

We're Getting in Shape—Bulletin Board

For the bulletin board background, post large shapes, each cut from a different color of paper. Use whatever shapes you have studied in class. Give students a shape cutout. Have them glue it to a piece of paper and add details to depict shape characters "getting in shape." Ask each child to tell you where his or her shape character would go on the board.

Skills

- Recognize and match similar shapes
- Recognize the shapes of real objects
- Name and identify shapes: circle, triangle, square, rectangle
- Use shapes to make pictures
- Draw shapes

Learning Center

Draw attention to the learning center by hanging large colorful shapes from the ceiling. Add student art projects made from shapes. Display books about shapes, such as those listed on page 213. Include a variety of materials and activities that will encourage students to experiment with shapes:

- ▲ pattern blocks and task cards
- ▲ attribute blocks
- ▲ solid geometric shapes
- ▲ geoboards and rubber bands
- ▲ tangram materials
- ▲ flannelboard shapes for creating shape pictures
- ▲ rulers for drawing shapes
- ▲ shape templates and patterns
- ▲ building blocks

The following activities, described on pages 22–26, are also appropriate for independent center work: *Shape Outline Cards, Shape Rubbings, Trace and Cut, Build a Picture, Feely Box, Shape Search.*

Activities

Moving on Shapes

Materials
● sidewalk chalk

✎ Activity

Draw several giant shapes on the playground with chalk. Divide the class among the shapes and ask students to stand on the shape's perimeter. Have students travel around the shapes using different locomotor movements: tiptoe, hop, skip, slide, jump, take baby steps or giant steps. Stop periodically and let groups change shapes. It's fun to play an instrumental tape to accompany this activity.

As a variation, students stand inside the shapes until a leader calls out a command such as "Circles and squares change shapes." In this case, children inside the circle must change places with students inside the square. The leader tries to tag players when they are outside a shape.

Everybody Show Shapes

Materials
● precut paper shapes, 1 set per student

✎ Activity

Provide precut shapes, or have students use the templates from the *Trace and Cut* activity (page 24) to trace and cut a set of shapes. Ask the class to spread the shapes out on their desks. Hold up one shape. Ask students to find a shape that matches yours and to hold it up for you to see. Or, give verbal clues such as, "I'm thinking of a shape with three sides and three corners." Let students take turns being the leader.

Feely Box

Materials
- large cardboard box
- scissors/razor knife
- sturdy shapes made from wood, plastic, foam board, or heavy posterboard (at least 2 of each shape)

✎ Activity
Cut off one side of a cardboard box, and cut two hand holes on the opposite side. Place an assortment of sturdy shapes inside the box. This is an excellent activity for partners to do at a center. One child inserts her hands into the holes and tries to find two shapes that are alike. Her partner verifies her choice.

Shape Rubbings

Materials
- unlined paper
- peeled crayons
- variety of textured materials for shape patterns: posterboard, corrugated cardboard, textured wallpaper, sandpaper, fun fur, embossed paper
- scissors

✎ Activity
Cut shape patterns of various sizes from a variety of textured materials. Have students place a piece of paper over a chosen shape. Using the side of a peeled crayon, they rub on the paper until the shape appears. Students can vary the design by overlapping many colors and shapes.

Shape Outline Cards

Materials

- Shape Outline Cards (page 159), 1 set per student
- glue (white or fluorescent)
- sand or glitter (optional)

✎ Activity

Reproduce the Shape Outline Cards on tagboard or heavy paper. Have students trace the shape outline with white glue and sprinkle on sand or glitter while the glue is still wet. Let these dry completely. Students love to use fluorescent glue for this activity. Put these shapes at a center, along with a blindfold, and see if students can identify them by touch alone. Or enlarge the Shape Outline Cards and let students stitch on top of the shapes with yarn.

Build a Picture

Materials

- picture book about shapes (list on page 213)
- pattern blocks
- precut paper shapes
- 9" x 12" construction paper
- glue sticks or white glue

✎ Activity

Introduce this activity with a book, such as *Color Farm* or *Color Zoo* by Lois Ehlert, that has illustrations made up of shapes. Place pattern blocks at a center, and let students build pictures with the shapes. Provide precut shapes that match the pattern blocks in shape and size. Students can make a record of their shape pictures by gluing the paper shapes on construction paper. These make a nice bulletin board display.

Trace and Cut

Materials

- plastic lids from margarine tubs and other containers
- razor knife
- drawing paper
- pencils

✎ Activity

Prepare the templates for students to use at a center. Draw or trace shapes on the lids. If the shapes are small, two or three sizes may fit on each lid. Cut out the shapes with the razor knife. Students can learn to draw shapes by using the templates. They can also use them to draw shape pictures.

Look and Draw

Materials

- Shape Outline Cards (page 159), 1 set for teacher
- individual chalkboards or magic slates, 1 per student
- chalk

✎ Activity

Give each child an individual chalkboard and chalk. Briefly hold up a card showing a shape. Ask the class to draw the shape from memory and hold their chalkboards up for the teacher to see. Then try giving verbal clues only, such as "Draw a shape with four equal sides." Or give students a series of directions, such as "Draw a circle in the center of your board. Put a triangle on top of it. Make a square to the left."

Yummy Shapes

Materials

- small plastic knives
- slices of cheese, lunch meat, bread
- paper plates
- paper to cover work area

✎ Activity

Review cutting safety before introducing *Yummy Shapes*, an ideal small group activity. Give students one piece each of lunch meat and cheese, and two slices of bread. They can then stack the foods or cut them individually into different shapes. This makes a fun math activity and a yummy snack!

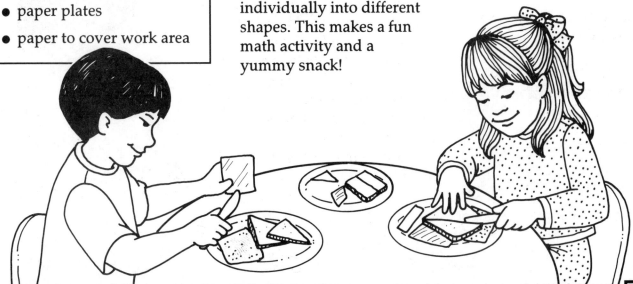

Shape Search

Materials

- old magazines, catalogs, newspapers
- scissors
- paper
- glue
- wide-tipped markers

✎ Activity

Place the materials at a center. Students search for shapes in the magazine ads and illustrations. Then they cut out a picture, glue it on a piece of paper, and trace the shape with a wide-tipped marker. A class big book or chart can be made out of the students' discoveries.

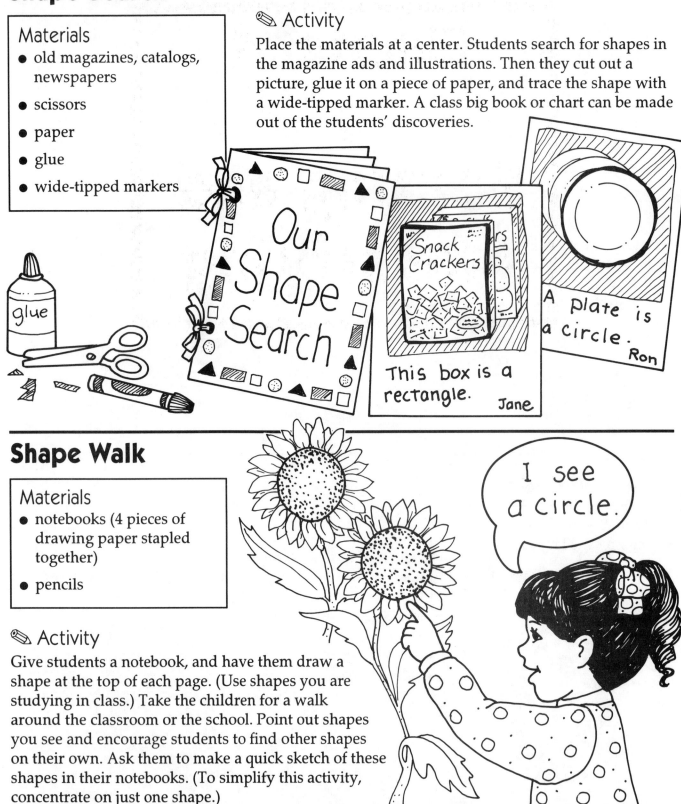

Shape Walk

Materials

- notebooks (4 pieces of drawing paper stapled together)
- pencils

✎ Activity

Give students a notebook, and have them draw a shape at the top of each page. (Use shapes you are studying in class.) Take the children for a walk around the classroom or the school. Point out shapes you see and encourage students to find other shapes on their own. Ask them to make a quick sketch of these shapes in their notebooks. (To simplify this activity, concentrate on just one shape.)

In the classroom, have students share their findings. Then make a class list on the chalkboard. Help the children discover which shapes are found most often in the objects around them.

Chapter 4

Sorting and Classifying

Sorting and Classifying

Sorting and classifying activities are valuable in the primary grades because they develop a child's ability to think in an analytical manner. This, in turn, leads to growth in the area of problem solving.

In order to sort and classify a group of objects, a child must be able to recognize common *attributes* of objects. For example, a nickel, a dime, and a quarter have several common attributes. They are all coins, they are all metal, and they are all round. The following activities use readily available materials and offer students a wide variety of experiences in sorting and classifying.

Classifying Our Class—Bulletin Board

Create a bulletin board that can be used to sort and classify the students in your room in a variety of ways: by hair color, height, eye color, clothing, number in family, or personal preferences. Divide the available bulletin board space into four or five large sections, and separate the sections with pieces of yarn.

Decide on a topic for sorting, hair color for example. Then label each section of the board with an appropriate attribute (brown hair, blond hair, etc.). Have students draw a self-portrait and tell you where it belongs on the bulletin board. Change the topic each week, and have students work together to sort the portraits.

Skills

- Observe similarities and differences
- Sort and classify objects by one attribute
- Sort and classify objects by more than one attribute
- Identify the sorting attribute(s)

Learning Center

After students have been introduced to sorting and classifying groups of objects, place the materials listed below at a center. Let students sort them according to the attributes they have chosen. For example, letter cards can be sorted by rounded/straight letters, capital/lowercase letters, tall/short letters.

- ▲ math collections for sorting (buttons, lids, bread tabs, seeds)
- ▲ paper plates, portion cups, margarine tubs to hold sorted materials
- ▲ flannelboard and felt shapes
- ▲ cards for labeling
- ▲ cards with numbers to 100
- ▲ cards with letters, uppercase and lowercase
- ▲ pattern blocks
- ▲ attribute blocks

Students can work alone, with a partner, or in small groups. They will especially enjoy sorting objects and having a friend "discover" the common attributes. Provide blank cards for students who want to label their sorted groups.

The following chapter activities are also suitable for center use: *Playing Card Sort, Our Favorite Sorting Game, Where Does It Belong?* (See pages 30–34.)

Activities

Looking Carefully

Materials
- paper plates, disposable microwave trays, or aluminum pie pans
- math collections (See pages 8 and 9.)

✎ Activity

Use this activity as an introduction to sorting and classifying. (The time you spend on any step of the activity will depend on the needs of your students.) Pick up one item, such as a button, from the math collections and hold it up for the class to see. Ask the class to tell you something they observe about it, such as "It's round." Put the button on a paper plate and tell the children that all round things will be put there. Choose another object from the math collections and ask, "Is it round or not round?" Place the item on a different plate.

Repeat this large group activity with a variety of objects and attributes. Then divide the class into small groups, and give each group paper plates and a collection of objects to sort. Have the children examine their collection and decide how it will be sorted. For example, buttons could be sorted by shape, color, number of holes, texture, or size. Circulate around the room and ask each group to tell you the attributes used. Then have students mix up their collection and sort it a different way.

Where Does It Belong?

Materials
- Picture Cards (page 160) or Creature Cards (page 161), 1 set per student
- scissors
- pencils

 Activity

Reproduce one set of Picture Cards (or Creature Cards) for each student. Have students cut the cards apart and write their name or initials on the back of each one. Then ask students to choose a partner, and have partners sit facing each other. Each child places his Picture Cards face down on the desk. The first child picks up one card and asks his partner, "Where does it belong?" The partner might respond, "with the animals," and they decide where to place the animal cards. The partner picks up one of her cards and asks the same question. Play continues until all the cards have been sorted into piles of animals, people, furniture, and kitchen utensils.

See if students can think of different ways to sort their cards, such as living/not living, noisy/quiet, hard/soft. You can also laminate a set of Picture Cards or Creature Cards and place them at a center for independent use.

Our Favorite Sorting Game

Materials
- food items to be sorted (jelly beans, cereal, trail mix)
- small paper cups, 1 per student
- 12" x 18" paper, 1 per student
- crayons/pencils

✎ Activity

Ask students to draw four circles (each about the size of a hand) on a large sheet of paper. Give each child a small cup of food items to be sorted. Students can choose how they will sort the items (by color, shape, size, taste, or type of food). For example, if they are sorting trail mix, their sorting categories might be nuts, raisins, M & M's®, and coconut.

When the sorting is completed, students record the contents of all four circles. For example, if there are four peanuts in one circle, they should draw four peanuts in the circle and eat the real peanuts. Try this with different food items as a center activity.

Sorting Toys

Materials
- assortment of stuffed animals (or other toys)

✎ Activity
Ask students to bring in a stuffed animal they can leave at school for a few days. As a group, make a list of attributes that describe the collection of animals (size, color, type of animal, length of tail, etc.). Select one or two attributes for use in sorting. Then ask the animal's owner to place his or her animal with the correct group.

Classifying Tastes

Materials
- an assortment of fruit cut in small pieces (apples, lemons, oranges, bananas, grapefruit, kiwis, pears, grapes, raisins)
- paper plates, 1 per student
- paper
- pencils

✎ Activity
The children will sort the fruit according to the tastes sweet and sour. Give students a plate of fruit samples and a piece of paper. Have them fold the paper in half and label one side "sweet" and the other side "sour." Take a piece of fruit and hold it up for the children to see. Have them find their matching fruit sample, repeat the name, and taste it. Ask the children whether it was sweet or sour. Have them make a drawing of that fruit in the corresponding section of the paper.

Repeat this process, with the other fruit samples. Discuss how students sorted their samples. Then let students sort their fruit samples in other ways (color, size, texture, like/dislike, shape).

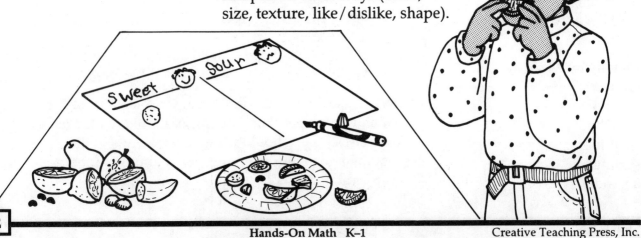

Hands-On Math K–1

Creative Teaching Press, Inc.

Sorting by Beginning Sounds

Materials
- 2–5 alphabet cards (for selected initial sounds)

✎ Activity

Lay the selected alphabet cards on the floor. Then have each student find something in the classroom that begins with one of the letters. If possible, students should place their objects under the correct letters. (Children can draw pictures for very large objects.) Repeat the activity using other letters of the alphabet.

Playing Card Sort

Materials
- playing cards, 1 deck for each group
- 2 hula hoops (optional)

✎ Activity

Divide the class into groups of three or four students, and give each group a deck of cards. The children decide how they will sort the cards. When sorting is completed, one student in each group tells how the cards were sorted. Then the groups select a different attribute and sort the cards again. This activity also works well at a center.

Playing cards can also be used to introduce sorting into overlapping sets to a small group of students. Lay down two hula hoops and designate a different attribute for each group, for example red cards in one and face cards in another. Have students take turns sorting the cards until you come to a red face card. Ask where it should be placed. Accept student suggestions, and try their ideas. Hopefully, someone will suggest overlapping the hoops. Have students continue sorting and explaining their choices. Repeat this type of activity using different materials. This is a good way to introduce the concept of a Venn diagram.

What's My Rule?

Materials
- none

✎ Activity

Ask four or five children with a common attribute to stand in front of the class. Start with an obvious attribute, such as all girls or all boys, and progress to more subtle ones, such as button shirts, missing front teeth, or names starting with a "J." Have classmates try to guess "the rule" for sorting. When the class becomes expert at this game, create a group with two common attributes, such as tall students with tie shoes. Then let children take turns being the leader.

Read and Sort

Materials
- book, *Goldilocks and the Three Bears*
- set of objects in three sizes
- basket or box
- work space, divided into three sections

✎ Activity

Read aloud your favorite edition of *Goldilocks and the Three Bears*. On a second reading, have students look for all the objects in the story that come in three sizes: small for Baby Bear, medium-sized for Mama Bear, and large for Papa Bear. Gather sets of small, medium, and large objects and place them at a center so students can sort them independently as shown below.

Chapter 5

Patterns

Patterns

The study of mathematics involves the ability to recognize the underlying patterns in our number system. Readiness for this skill can be developed by providing many experiences in the patterning of objects. The activities in this chapter offer opportunities for analyzing the different elements in a pattern, reproducing sample patterns, and creating original patterns.

We Love Looking for Patterns!—Bulletin Board

Create an eye-catching bulletin board display that encourages students to look for patterns. Have the class use fluorescent shape cutouts to make patterns on black paper strips. Post these on the bulletin board. Older students can also write their patterns with letters on manila paper. Store these in a box or envelope. Classmates can choose a letter pattern strip and match it to one of the shape patterns on the board. Sponge paint or use calendar cutouts to create a repeated pattern on the border.

Skills

- Identify patterns in the environment
- Identify patterns in numbers
- Copy patterns
- Extend patterns
- Make new patterns

Learning Center

The pattern learning center will give students opportunities to make patterns on an independent, informal basis. Make a sign for the center that is bordered with a pattern. Provide lots of materials, such as those listed below, so students can experiment with making, extending, and recording patterns. Allow bulletin board space for posting student-made patterns.

- ▲ construction paper shape cutouts
- ▲ rubber stamps
- ▲ stamp pads
- ▲ stickers
- ▲ plastic linking cubes
- ▲ pattern blocks
- ▲ math collections
- ▲ strips of paper
- ▲ pencils/crayons/markers

The following chapter activities lend themselves to learning center use: *Pattern Copycat, Playdough Patterns, Object Pattern Cards, Letter Pattern Cards, Unfinished Patterns,* and *Necklace Patterns.* (See pages 38–42.)

Activities

Patterning Ourselves

Materials
● none

✎ Activity

Choose several children to stand in the front of the room, and sequence them so a pattern will be formed. (For example, a child wearing pants, one wearing a skirt, one wearing pants, etc.) Have the class try to guess what the pattern is. After the children return to their seats, repeat the activity with different patterns: sport shoes/dress shoes, long hair/short hair, blue eyes/brown eyes, teeth missing/no teeth missing. Next have a child select a pattern and choose the students to represent the pattern.

Shoe Patterns

Materials
● students' shoes

✎ Activity

Working together as a group, make different patterns using students' shoes. Different pattern elements include the shoe's type, color, position, material, and size.

Patterned Noises

Materials
● none

✎ Activity

Clap and snap your fingers in a sound pattern, initially chanting, "clap, snap, clap, snap . . ." Have the children join in when they understand what you are doing. Repeat the same sequence saying, "A, B, A, B . . ." Once students have the idea, vary the AB AB pattern using claps, finger snaps, intervals of silence, and other auditory signals. On subsequent days, try a sequence of sounds with an ABC ABC pattern, an AA BB pattern, and so on.

Matching Moving Patterns

Materials

- none

✎ Activity

Select a child to present a pattern to the class using different body movements, such as step, jump, step, jump. The child then calls on a classmate to repeat the pattern using different movements, such as arms up, arms down, arms up, arms down. You can involve the whole class by having them verbalize the patterns and/or perform the movement patterns with the leader.

Pattern Copycat

Materials
- math collections (See pages 8 and 9.)
- pencils
- strips of unlined paper

✎ Activity

Distribute the math collections and ask students to use the objects to make a pattern. Challenge them to create several different patterns using the same materials. As an extension, have them draw a picture of one pattern on a paper strip. Younger students can verbalize the pattern, and older students can label their patterns with letters.

Make One Like Mine

Materials
- pattern blocks
- overhead projector
- math collections (See pages 8 and 9.)

✎ Activity

Using the overhead projector and pattern blocks, make a pattern on the screen and ask the class to identify it. If the pattern is AB AB, students use the math collections to make an AB AB pattern on their desks, while the teacher circulates to assess understanding. Choose a child to make the next pattern on the screen.

Playdough Patterns

Materials
- playdough in various colors
- mini-cookie cutters
- rolling pin
- plastic to cover work area

✎ Activity

Students roll out the dough, cut out shapes, and place the shapes in a pattern. When the pattern is complete, they can ask a friend to identify it.

Object Pattern Cards

Materials
- Object Pattern Cards (pages 162 and 163)
- pennies, nickels, rubber bands, large and small paper clips, toothpicks, straws
- blank cards
- pencils/markers

✎ Activity

Cut the cards apart and laminate them. Place the cards and collections of the everyday objects pictured on the cards at a center. Students can extend the patterns on the cards using the concrete objects. Encourage students to make their own object pattern cards to add to the collections.

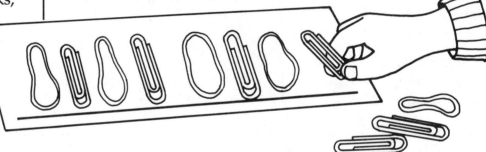

Letter Pattern Cards

Materials
- Letter Pattern Cards (pages 164 and 165)
- math collections (See pages 8 and 9.)

✎ Activity

Cut the cards apart and laminate them. Place all materials at a center. Have students use the math collections to make patterns that match the letter pattern cards.

Unfinished Patterns

Materials

- pre-cut shapes in various colors and sizes
- strips of paper (dimensions may vary), 1 per student
- glue

✎ Activity

Pass out the materials and have students glue some of the pre-cut shapes in a pattern on the strip. Have students give their unfinished pattern to a partner or neighbor, who will complete the pattern to the end of the strip. The unfinished patterns could also be collected and placed at a center.

Stamping Patterns

Materials

- strips of butcher paper, 1 per student
- rubber stamps, several for each group
- stamp pads, 1 or 2 for each group

✎ Activity

Divide the class into groups of four or five students. Give each group several stamps and a stamp pad. Each child stamps a pattern (one repetition only) on a strip and then passes his strip to the student on his right. This child adds the next piece of the pattern and passes the pattern to her right. This procedure continues until the strip is complete. Have students check the patterns for accuracy.

Necklace Patterns

Materials

- 32" pieces of yarn or string, 1 per student
- drinking straws cut in 1" pieces
- small construction paper shapes (variety of colors)
- hole punch

✎ Activity

Place all materials at a center. Punch or let the children punch a hole in the center of each paper shape. Students string the straw pieces and the shapes in a pattern. Tie the ends of the string and you have a wearable pattern!

Pattern Walk

Materials
- note pads (several sheets of paper stapled together), 1 per student
- pencils

✎ Activity

Give each child a note pad and take a walk around the classroom to look for patterns. (For example, the alphabet display with alternating uppercase and lowercase letters, or a child's striped shirt with alternating red, white, and blue stripes.)

Encourage each student to find at least three patterns and to draw pictures of the patterns on his or her note pad. Let students share their patterns, then assemble the note pad pages into a class book of patterns. On another day, try a pattern walk around the school grounds.

Language Patterns

Materials
- book, *It Looked Like Spilt Milk* by Charles Shaw
- small bags of 10 or more common objects (pencil, rock, marker, shell, eraser, etc.), 1 set per group
- cotton balls, 1 per group

✎ Activity

After reading the story, ask students if they can find the repeated language pattern. (*Sometimes it looked like a _____. But it wasn't a _____.*) Provide small groups of children with a bag of common objects. As students select an object from the bag, they should use the same language pattern as in the story. For example, "Sometimes it looked like a rock. But it wasn't a rock." The activity ends with the cotton ball, and the whole group recites together, "It was just a cloud in the sky."

The list of books on page 215 includes many other books with repetitive language patterns. If you can find some titles in big book form, students can see the repetitive language pattern in print. Place the big book at a center and let students use a pointer to track the language pattern.

Chapter 6

Numbers and Counting

Numbers and Counting

The ability to count with understanding involves three separate but sequentially related skills: (1) rote counting—counting by memorizing a sequence of words; (2) one-to-one correspondence—matching number names to the objects in a set; (3) conservation of number—an understanding that although the arrangement of a set of objects may differ, the quantity remains the same. Children develop competence in these areas when they are given repeated opportunities to count sets of objects. These experiences help establish the link between rote counting and other number concepts.

You Can Count on Us—Bulletin Board

Use this bulletin board to celebrate growth in counting skills. Prepare the following cutouts for the whole class: smile, pair of eyes, hand, pair of feet with toes. (See reproducible pages 166 and 167.) Divide the available bulletin board space into four parts, labeling the sections 1s, 2s, 5s, 10s. Each time a student demonstrates a new counting skill, write the child's name on the appropriate cutout and place it on the board. Be sure to give students practice in these skills every day so that all of the children will eventually be successful in all skill areas.

Skills

- One-to-one correspondence
- Count to 100 by ones
- Count to 100 by fives and tens
- Count backward from 20
- Skip count by twos
- Compare equal and unequal sets
- Find the number that comes before, after, and between

Learning Center

Provide a wide variety of objects for counting such as those listed below. When students are skilled at counting by ones, encourage them to group objects and count by twos, fives, or tens. They can use the Counting Recording Sheet (page 169) to record these experiences.

- manipulatives bagged in sets of 10 and 20
- math manipulatives to be counted in large quantities
- math collections
- small paper cups
- wooden beads (string and count)
- pennies and a bank
- plastic linking cubes (snap together and count)
- pattern blocks

Include a selection of counting books so students can read and count. (See page 216 for a list of book titles.) Post a hundreds chart low enough so children can touch each number. Purchase or make a walk-on number line so children can count in a kinesthetic style. (Use heavy plastic colored tape and a permanent marker to make the number line.)

The following chapter activities would also work well at a center: *Counting by Ones, Counting by Twos Grab Bag, Number Shuffle, Copy My Number.* (See pages 46–52.)

Activities

Let the needs of your students dictate how high you ask children to count in the following activities.

Counting by Ones

Materials
- pennies and bank with removable stopper
- plastic linking cubes
- wooden beads and strings

✎ **Activity**

Work on rote counting and one-to-one correspondence with this activity. Divide the children into groups of two or three and give each group one set of objects (pennies, cubes, or beads). The children count in unison by ones as they drop pennies into a bank, snap together linking cubes, or string beads.

1, 2, 3, 4, 5...

Counting to Music

Materials
- recorded music
- tape player or record player

✎ **Activity**

Combine music, movement, and math skills when you play this game. Turn on some lively music with a steady beat. As the music plays, call out directions like the following: "Tap your nose 10 times." "Knock your knees and count by twos." "March in place to 25." Have students count out loud as they follow the directions and move to the music.

18, 19, 20...

Counting On

Materials
- Number Cards (page 168)
- hat or box

✎ Activity

Place the number cards in a hat. Ask a child to select one card and show it to the class. Have students say that number out loud and then continue counting on in unison. Reinforce learning by adding a movement, such as tapping heads or clapping hands in one-to-one correspondence with each number. As the year progresses, practice counting on with larger numbers.

Count, Count, Count

Materials
- multiples of inexpensive objects (beans, buttons, macaroni, toothpicks, seeds)
- small paper cups

✎ Activity

Divide the children into groups of three or four. Give each group 10 paper cups and objects, such as beans, to count. Then ask students to count out 10 beans in each cup. When they are finished, the teacher moves around the room, counting with the class by tens to determine how many beans there were for each group. Have students repeat this activity counting by fives.

Number Line Walk

Materials

- chalk number line (1–20) drawn on playground or sidewalk

✎ Activity

This is a good small group activity that students can do at recess after it has been modeled in class. Starting on 2, have students step on every other number, saying each number out loud: "two, four, six, eight . . . ." For older students, you may want to extend the number line into higher numbers. Or, teach them to start on the number 1 and skip count by twos on all the odd numbers: "one, three, five, seven . . . ."

Counting by Twos Grab Bag

Materials

- math collections (See pages 8 and 9.)
- paper bags

✎ Activity

Divide the class into groups of two or three. Give each group a grab bag filled with math manipulatives. Have one child grab a handful of objects and place them in the center of the work area. Ask students to arrange the objects in pairs and count them by twos. After each member of the group has had a turn, students grab two handfuls of objects and count those by twos.

It's Your Turn

Materials
● none

✎ Activity

Start counting out loud by ones, twos, fives, or tens. Then "pass" the counting by touching a student on the shoulder. The teacher sits in the child's seat, and the student continues counting where the teacher left off, until another student is tapped on the shoulder, and so on. This game can also be played with partners or in a small group setting.

Counting Backward

Materials
● book, *Mooncake* by Frank Asch

✎ Activity

After reading *Mooncake*, review the part of the story where Bear begins the count-down for his rocket ship to the moon. Then invite your class to sit on the floor, count backward from 10, and blast off (jump up) as they say "zero!"

Next, try this fun counting game. Stand in front of the class facing the students and ask them to count by ones slowly and in unison. Tell them that when you turn your back to them, they are to stop counting forward and begin counting backward. When you turn to face them again, they are to count forward again. For example, if the class is counting "zero, one, two, three, four," and you turn around, they start counting backward "three, two, one, zero." Once the class has the idea, choose a child to direct the counting.

Vary the activity by having students stand as they count. When you give an auditory signal, such as ringing a bell, they are to turn around and count backward.

Count Up, Count Down

Materials
- none

✎ Activity
Each child selects a partner. Then the partners take turns counting forward and backward. As ability increases, on every third turn, the child can choose whether to continue counting forward or change to counting backward, or vice versa.

Number Shuffle

Materials
- Number Cards (page 168), 1 set per student
- scissors
- timer

✎ Activity
Students cut the cards apart and place them face up on their desks. Cards must be mixed up. (At first use just 1–10.) When a signal is given, students unscramble their cards, place them in numerical order, then raise their hands. When a child is able to do this in less than two minutes, he or she can repeat the activity using all the cards (1–20). The two-minute time limit may change depending on students' needs.

Before, After, or Between

Materials
- large number cards (1–10), 1 set for teacher
- pocket chart
- Number Cards (page 168), 1 set per student
- scissors

✎ Activity
Place the demonstration number cards in a pocket chart or on the chalk ledge so all students can see them. Have the children take turns finding the number that comes "after five," "before one," "between eight and ten." Let students try the same activity with a partner using the reproducible Number Cards on page 168. After they have mastered numbers to 10, repeat with numbers to 20.

Copy My Number

Materials
- sets of manipulatives (shells, rocks, beans, etc.), 20 per student
- pencils

✎ Activity

Divide the class into pairs. Give each partner a different kind of manipulative. Have one student make a set of ten or less. The child's partner must duplicate the number with his or her objects. Then the children match the objects one-to-one to show that the sets are equivalent. Repeat using different quantities each time.

Can You Match Me?

✎ Activity

Draw a set of objects on the board or overhead and count the number of objects with the class. Now have the children use manipulatives to make sets with the same number of objects. When all children have formed their sets, count together to check. After repeating this several times, have them make a set with "one more" than your set. Repeat, requesting a set containing "one less" than your set. Monitor their responses by circulating around the room, helping as needed. A child could also lead this activity, after it has been modeled.

Materials
- chalkboard or overhead projector
- manipulatives, 10 per student

One more than five is six.

Conservation of Number—An Assessment Activity

It is essential to complete this assessment with every child before
progressing to more difficult number concepts.

Materials
- 5 objects (blocks or plastic milk bottle lids work well)

✎ Activity

Hold five objects in one hand. Working with one student at a
time, show her the five objects you are holding. Tell her that
you are holding five objects. Now put some of these objects
in the other open hand. Ask how many objects you are
holding now. Of course, the total number of objects has not
changed, only their arrangement or grouping. If she must
count them in order to answer, she does not understand this
concept and needs more practice.

Once she understands that the number of objects remains the
same regardless of how they are grouped, she has grasped
the concept of conservation and is ready to proceed to more
difficult number activities.

Chapter 7

Writing Numerals

Writing Numerals

Writing a numeral is a relatively refined skill because it involves both recognition of the symbol and the translation of its mental picture into motor actions. In order to recognize or read a symbol, the child must know what makes it different from other symbols. Point out the different strokes involved in writing the numeral. This provides a "motor plan" for numeral formation which is necessary for consistent, correct formation of numerals.

Hands-on Numerals—Bulletin Board

Use the pictures created by students in the *Feely Numerals* activity (page 56) for a textured bulletin board display that is sure to have "hands-on" appeal. Have students sign their pictures and write or dictate a sentence telling how their number feels. Mount or frame each picture using brightly colored paper.

Skills

- Identify numerals

- Write numerals

Learning Center

Hang giant numerals from the ceiling to draw attention to the learning center. Stock the shelves with "touchable" numerals in all shapes, sizes, and materials. Try numerals made from felt, sandpaper, fun fur, cotton balls, napped fabric, embossed wrapping paper, or corrugated cardboard. Add some of the numeral cards that students have made in the *Glue Numerals* activity (page 56). Any of these tactile numerals could be used with a blindfold for a guessing game.

Students can make rubber band numerals on geoboards or arrange pattern blocks and tangrams to form numerals. (You might want to provide patterns to follow.) They can draw numerals on magic slates and mini-chalkboards or form numerals with pieces of yarn, toothpicks, or playdough.

In addition, the following chapter activities offer fun ways to practice numeral formation: *Salt/Sand Box, Numeral Rubbings, Disappearing Numerals, Snake Numerals, Numeral in a Bag.* (See pages 56–60.)

Activities

Feely Numerals

Materials

- numeral outlines duplicated on 9" x 12" tagboard, 1 per student (Or enlarge numerals on reproducible page 170.)
- various materials to glue (popcorn, Styrofoam packing materials, cotton balls, beans, rice, pieces of yarn, macaroni)
- white glue
- crayons

✎ Activity

Provide students with numeral outlines. Have each child identify his or her numeral and draw a matching set of objects in the space around it. Next, ask students to glue a textured material on the numeral. Let these dry for a couple of days. Use them to create a textured bulletin board or wall display. (See page 54.)

Glue Numerals

Materials

- glue, white or colored
- 2" x 3" pieces of acetate, 1 per student
- Numeral Patterns (page 170), optional

✎ Activity

Students use glue to draw a numeral on their piece of acetate. Let the glue dry completely and use the Glue Numerals at a learning center for a tactile guessing game. Children love to use fluorescent glue for this activity. The fluorescent numerals look great displayed in a window.

For children who need more support, provide a copy of the Numeral Patterns reproducible. Students can lay their acetate directly on the pattern and trace over a numeral.

Salt/Sand Box

Materials

- flat-bottomed plastic container and lid, approximately 6" x 6"

- black construction paper

- fine sand or salt, enough to fully cover the bottom of the container ¹/₄" deep

✎ Activity

Line the bottom of a plastic sandwich keeper with a single sheet of black paper. Fill the container with ¹/₄" of salt. The student removes the lid and gently moves the container from side to side to even out the salt. She draws a numeral in the sand, which separates to allow the black paper to be seen in the shape of the numeral drawn. Then she "clears" the sand and draws other numerals.

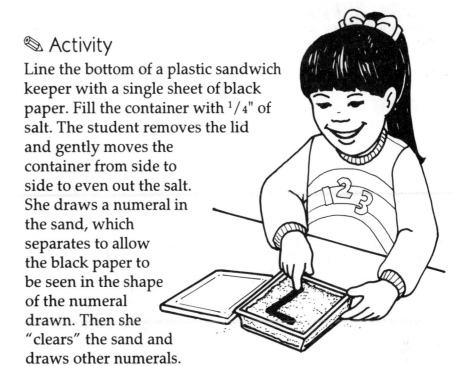

Numeral Rubbings

Materials

- numerals (1–9) cut out of posterboard, corrugated cardboard, sandpaper, embossed wrapping paper, or other textured materials

- Numeral Patterns (page 170)

- crayons with paper peeled off

- 9" x 12" newsprint or other thin paper, 1 per student

- 6" x 36" strips of newsprint, 1 per student

✎ Activity

Use the patterns on page 170 to cut numerals from a variety of textured materials. (You can enlarge the patterns on a copier to vary the size of the numerals.) Have students place a textured numeral on the desk and put the paper on top. Using the side of the crayon, they rub back and forth over the numeral until the "rubbing" of the entire numeral is visible. After students have experimented with this technique, have them make a rubbing of all the numerals in order on a long strip of paper. You can also leave the tactile patterns at an art center so students can make beautiful numeral designs.

Disappearing Numerals

Materials

- paintbrushes
- cups of water
- individual chalkboards

✎ Activity

Have the children "paint" numerals of varying sizes on their mini-chalkboards. When the water evaporates, they can repeat the activity. At recess, they can move outside and paint numerals on sidewalks, walls, and blacktop surfaces using house paintbrushes and water.

Snake Numerals

Materials

- modeling clay or playdough
- plastic place mats to work on

✎ Activity

Have the children roll the clay into long "snakes" and practice forming the numerals 0–9. (Students who need more support can form the numeral on top of a laminated numeral card.) This tactile experience reinforces numeral formation and recognition.

Edible Numerals

Materials

- refrigerator biscuits
- baking sheets
- pot holders
- oven
- shortening for greasing pan and hands
- paper towels

✎ Activity

Have students grease their hands, roll the biscuit dough into coils, and form numerals with the coils of dough. You can follow the baking instructions on the roll of biscuits, but you will probably need to slightly decrease the baking time. Delicious dunked in honey or jam!

Body Writing

Materials

- none

✎ Activity

Using their "finger pencils" (pointer fingers held straight like a pencil), students take turns writing numerals on each other's backs and guessing which numeral has been drawn.

Write and Clean

Materials

- shaving cream
- damp sponge or paper towels

✎ Activity

Squirt a dollop of shaving cream on each child's desk. Students smooth out the shaving cream and practice writing numerals in it until the shaving cream "disappears." Wipe with a damp sponge and you have a clean desk top!

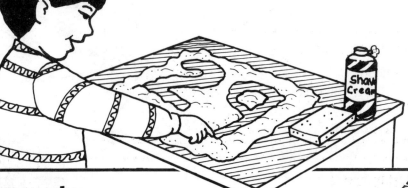

Sidewalk Numerals

Materials

- large sheets of newsprint, 1 per student
- crayons with paper peeled off

✎ Activity

Students lay the newsprint on a sidewalk (or other textured surface) and practice writing large numerals with the side of a crayon. They can trade crayons for a variety of colors.

Walk the Numeral

Materials
- sidewalk chalk or masking tape

✎ Activity
Using chalk outside or masking tape in the room, form three-foot-tall numerals. On each one indicate the starting point with an "X." Have students walk the numeral just as it would be written.

Rainbow Writing

Materials
- crayons in rainbow colors
- unlined paper

✎ Activity
Have students write the numerals they want to practice on plain paper. Then ask them to trace over each numeral with several colors to create a rainbow effect. You may want to provide a pattern for students who are not sure of correct numeral formation.

Numeral in a Bag

Materials
- small self-sealing plastic bags
- tempera paint or finger paint

✎ Activity
Put paint into self-sealing bags and close securely. Students practice "finger painting" numerals on the surface of the plastic bag. It's a fun way to practice, and there's no mess to clean up!

Chapter 8
Addition

Addition

Children who are beginning to explore the concept of addition need repeated experiences joining sets of concrete objects. Throughout these activities, encourage students to verbalize their actions so that addition language patterns will be established. When children demonstrate an understanding of combining sets, model how addition problems can be recorded first with pictures, and then symbolically with numbers. Remember to use both horizontal and vertical notation. Students need to use a wide variety of materials for all of these addition investigations.

How Many All Together?—Bulletin Board

Create an interactive bulletin board where students can make up and solve addition problems. Select an area that children can reach easily, and put up a blank addition equation using circles for the addends and a square for the sum. Have the class collect magazine or catalog pictures that fit a theme such as toys, fruits and vegetables, flowers, cars, or animals. Glue these pictures onto cards. Provide a large envelope for the cards and an envelope with several sets of the numerals 0 to 9. Encourage students to work in pairs to make up addition problems. One student pins up the picture addends, and the other puts up the matching numerals and the sum.

Skills

- Understand the meaning of addition

- Combine sets

- Find sums less than 10

- Draw pictures to solve addition problems

- Write addition equations

Addition Learning Center

Center activities will be a natural outgrowth of the *Exploring Combinations* activity described on page 64. Offer a wide variety of materials that students can use for combining sets, such as class math collections, plastic linking cubes, pattern blocks, beans and cups, toothpicks, bingo chips, flannelboard cutouts, and numerals.

Provide alternative ways for students to record their findings. Inexpensive materials like beans or toothpicks can be glued on paper. Students can draw pictures of concrete sets or make cut-and-paste pictures that represent number combinations. They can also use rubber stamps to create pictorial addition problems.

Include books about addition, like *The Doorbell Rang* by Pat Hutchins and *Addition Annie* by David Gisler. (See page 217 for more titles.) Provide flash cards for students who are working on the symbolic level.

The following chapter activities would also be appropriate for use at the learning center: *Domino Dots, Seed Addition, Edible Addition, Story Problem Listening Center, Addition Pictures, Addition Collage.* (See pages 64–70.)

Activities

Exploring Combinations

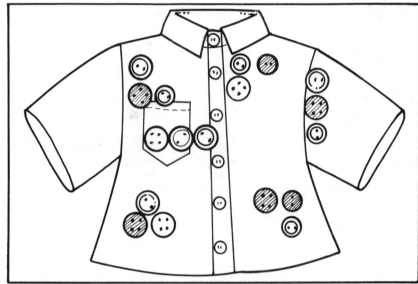

Materials

- math collections (See pages 8 and 9.)
- Work Space Cards (pages 176–178), 1 per student
- tagboard or construction paper
- paper (for recording)
- pencils, crayons

✎ Activity

Reproduce the Work Space Cards on tagboard or construction paper. (You may want to enlarge each one to a 9" x 12" size). Give each student a set of manipulatives and a card to work on. Have students use manipulatives to discover the many different patterns and combinations that can be made for a specific number. Start with "3" and progress to other numbers when students are ready. (Be sure they explore each number with a variety of manipulatives.) For example, one child found six different ways to arrange buttons in sets of three (shown above).

Encourage students to describe their combinations. ("I used three buttons. Two are on the bottom and one is on the top.") Later, students can make drawings to record their number combinations. This step connects concrete experiences with the more abstract illustrations. Finally, encourage those who are ready to record their work in the form of a number sentence.

Number Sentences, Part 1—Invasion of the Ants

Materials

- plastic ants, 5 per student (Or use the Ant reproducible on page 173.)
- Ant Work Space Card (page 172), 1 per student

✎ Activity

Give each child a copy of the Ant Work Space Card and five ants. (Plastic ants can be purchased at a party supply or craft store.) Have students place all five ants on the picture of the sandwich. Working with the whole class, ask the following questions: How many ants are there on the sandwich? (5) How many are on the lemonade? (0) How many ants does that make altogether? (5) Have the children repeat with you, "Five plus zero equals five."

Now move one ant over to the lemonade. Ask the same questions as above and model the oral number sentence: "Four plus one equals five." Continue until all ants are on the right side and your number sentence is "Zero plus five equals five."

On another day, repeat the activity using a set of six ants. As students verbalize the addition problems, model how to write the corresponding equations in both vertical and horizontal formats.

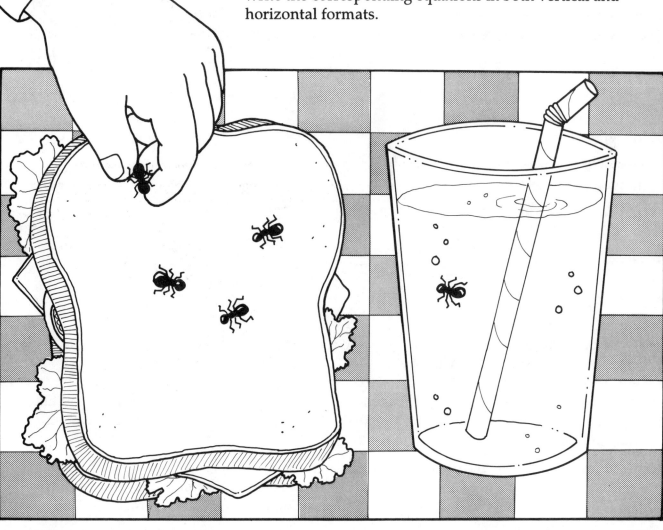

Number Sentences, Part 2—More Ants

Materials

- plastic ants, 7–10 per student (Or use Ant reproducible on page 173.)
- Ant Work Space Card (page 172), 1 per student
- paper
- pencils

✏ Activity

Have students place all seven ants on the sandwich side of the card, and ask for the corresponding number sentence (7 + 0 = 7). Write this on the chalkboard. Ask students to copy the equation on their paper. Continue in this fashion, modeling both vertical and horizontal notation, until all the equations for 7 have been covered.

On another day, have students work independently to build and write number sentences for 8. Circulate as students work, offering support to those who need it. Collect the papers for evaluation. On subsequent days have students work individually with the ant manipulatives and record the corresponding number sentences for 9 and 10.

Any Order You Want

Materials

- plastic ants, 10 per student (Or use Ant reproducible on page 173.)
- Ant Work Space Card (page 172), 1 per student
- paper or individual chalkboards
- pencils or chalk

✏ Activity

Have students place five ants on the sandwich and two ants on the glass of lemonade. Ask for the total number of ants and write the equation (5 + 2 = 7) on the board. Have students reverse the order of the sets, placing two ants on the sandwich and five ants on the lemonade. After students give you the total again, write the equation (2 + 5 = 7) and ask why the answers are the same. Repeat with different combinations, such as 1 + 6 and 6 + 1.

When students are able to verbalize the "order doesn't matter rule," ask them to work in pairs. One child makes two sets of ants and then reverses the order. The second child records both equations on an individual chalkboard or on paper. Students then switch roles.

People Problems

Materials

- chalkboard
- chalk
- Little People® dolls by Fisher-Price (optional)

✎ Activity

Have students take turns telling and acting out story problems that involve class members. For example, "Jeremy, Keri, and Janet were playing catch. Sam and Erica joined them. How many kids are playing catch now?" Let the designated students act out the problem. Another student can record the number sentence on the chalkboard.

If you can gather a collection of Fisher-Price "Little People" dolls (inexpensive at garage sales), place them at a center and let pairs of students make up "Little People" story problems.

Domino Dots

Materials

- dominos (Or use Domino Dot Cards reproducible on page 174.)
- Domino Dots Recording Sheets (page 175), 1 per student
- pencils
- demonstration Domino Dot Cards, made by teacher
- chalk

✎ Activity

Prepare several class-sized "dominos" for demonstration purposes. Hold up one and ask students how many dots are in the top section and how many dots are in the bottom section. Write an equation on the chalkboard to reflect their response. Repeat with several other giant dominos. Then give each student a copy of the recording sheet and a few dominos. They are to record the dots from their dominos on the paper and write the corresponding equations under each one. Have students trade dominos and complete the rest of the recording sheet. This activity also works well at a center.

Seed Addition

Materials

- sunflower seeds in the shell
- index cards
- glue

✎ Activity

Give each student one or more index cards with a number sentence written on each card. They then take the appropriate number of sunflower seeds, arrange them to represent that number sentence, and glue the seeds into place. There are many different ways the seeds might be arranged. Students will also enjoy making up their own seed equations. This is a good learning center activity.

Edible Addition

Materials

- finger foods (dry cereals, pretzels, raisins, nuts, carrot slices)
- small paper plates, 1 per student
- paper cups, 1 per student
- paper
- crayons
- bowl, 1 per group

✎ Activity

Divide the class into groups of four or five students, and give each group a bowl of finger food. As one child tells a story problem, the others use the snack food as addition manipulatives. ("I ate three pretzels and my sister ate seven. How many did we eat in all?") Then they eat the food, and another child tells a new story problem. Afterwards, encourage students to draw food addition problems on their paper plates. Display these near the addition center.

Story Problem Listening Center

Materials

- tape recorder
- headsets
- recording of student-made story problems
- manipulatives
- Work Space Cards (pages 176–178), optional
- paper
- pencils or crayons

✎ Activity

Tape record each student telling an addition story problem and place the tape at a listening center. As students listen to the pre-recorded stories, they combine sets of manipulatives to match the problems. They can also record their addition combinations with pictures or equations.

Addition Pictures

Materials

- 2" x 3" slips of paper (approx. 30)
- crayons or markers
- drawing paper

✎ Activity

Write an equation on each slip of paper. Have students choose one equation and write or glue it on the back of their drawing paper. Then they draw an appropriate picture on the front of the paper. For example, for the equation 3 + 2 = 5, a figure holding three balloons can be drawn with another figure approaching and holding two balloons. Have students share their addition pictures with the class, and see if the class can tell the equation used.

$$3 + 2 = 5$$

Addition Collage

Materials

- 9" x 12" construction paper
- collage materials such as ribbon, felt, foil, paper scraps
- glue
- pencils

✎ Activity

Integrate art and math by having students use collage materials to illustrate addition problems. For example, if the equation is 3 + 2 = 5, a child might choose two pieces of fabric and three pieces of ribbon and glue them on the paper in a pleasing design. The equation should be written on the paper, too. These collages make an attractive bulletin board display.

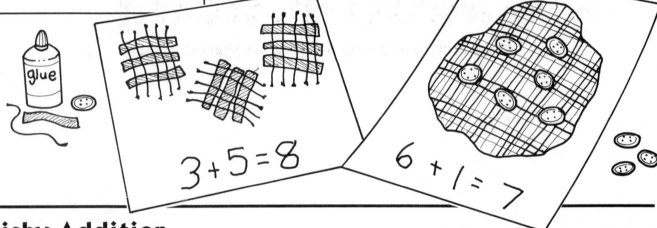

$$3 + 5 = 8$$

$$6 + 1 = 7$$

Fishy Addition

Material

- fish-shaped crackers
- napkins, 1 per student
- paper cups, 1 per student
- book, *Fish Eyes* by Lois Ehlert

✎ Activity

Give students a small cup of fish-shaped crackers. As you read aloud *Fish Eyes* by Lois Ehlert, students can re-create the addition problems depicted in the story. Of course, let the children eat any fish they catch!

Chapter 9
❧
Subtraction

Subtraction

When introducing subtraction, offer a wide variety of experiences in separating sets of concrete objects. Encourage students to verbalize these experiences so they develop language patterns for subtraction (*left, take away, remain, minus*). When students know how to separate sets using manipulatives, show them how to record—first pictorially, and then symbolically—with number sentences. Remember to model both horizontal and vertical format.

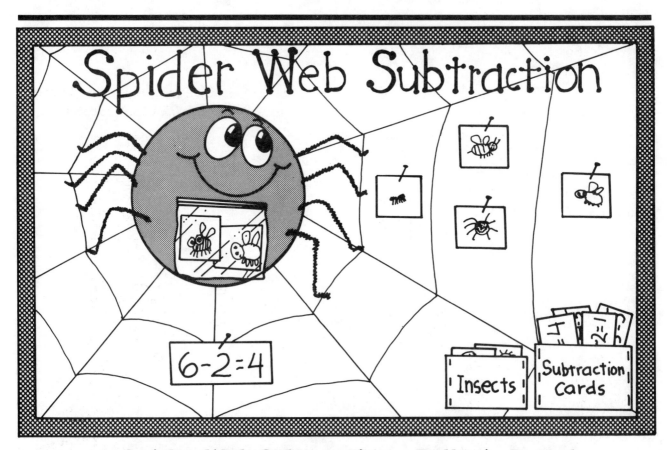

Spider Web Subtraction—Bulletin Board

Staple a black yarn spider web to a white background, and add a large construction paper spider. Staple a self-sealing plastic bag on the spider's stomach so it can "eat" the insects. Have students color and cut out a variety of insects, and place them in an envelope on or near the board, along with a set of subtraction equation cards. Students choose an equation card and illustrate the equation by pinning up the correct number of insects as shown.

Hands-On Math K–1   Creative Teaching Press, Inc.

Skills

- Understand what finding the "difference" means

- Explore subtraction facts to 10 with manipulatives

- Draw pictures to solve subtraction problems

- Use symbols to record subtraction problems

Learning Center

Stock the center with a wide variety of materials that students can use for separating sets: pattern blocks, plastic linking cubes, felt figures and flannelboard, wooden cubes, and student math collections (pages 8 and 9). Students might also enjoy using the Work Space Cards used in Chapter 8 (pages 176–178).

As in the Addition Center, give students alternative ways to record their investigations: paper, crayons, markers, rubber stamps, cut-and-paste materials. Include books about subtraction such as those listed on page 218. Provide flash cards for students who are working on the symbolic level.

The following chapter activities would also be appropriate for use at a learning center: *Recording Subtraction, 3-D Subtraction Problems,* and *Sorting Pennies.* (See pages 74–78.)

Activities

Acting Out Subtraction Problems

Materials
● none

✎ Activity

Model this activity with the whole group, then divide the class into groups of four or five children. Ask each group to make up a subtraction story and pantomime or dramatize the story for the class. The audience tries to retell the story and gives the answer to the subtraction problem. For example: "There were four children sitting on the floor playing a board game (four children sit on the floor). Two of them had to go home early (two children get up and walk away). How many children are left?"

Sorting People for Subtraction

Materials
● none

✎ Activity

Select a group of students who can eventually be sorted into two subgroups; for example, blond students and brown-haired students. Have the class count the number of students in the group. Ask the children with blond hair to move to the other side of the classroom. Then have the class verbalize the subtraction problem: "Five take away two equals three." You can also write the problem on the chalkboard (5 - 2 = 3). Repeat the activity, sorting by various attributes and letting students take the teacher's role.

Subtraction Number Sentences, Part 1—One by One

Materials

- plastic ants, 5 per student (or use the Ant reproducible on page 173)
- Basket Work Space Card (page 179), 1 per student

✎ Activity

Give each child five ants and a copy of the Basket Work Space Card. Ask students to place all five ants in the middle of the picnic basket. Have them remove one ant and put it on the desk. Recite together: "Five take away one equals four." Remove another ant and say, "Five take away two equals three." Continue until all the ants are taken away and the number sentence is, "Five take away five equals zero."

On another day, repeat the activity using a set of six ants. As students verbalize the subtraction problems, model how to write the corresponding equations in both vertical and horizontal formats.

Subtraction Number Sentences, Part 2—Take Them Away

Materials

- plastic ants, 7-10 per student (or use the Ant reproducible on page 173)
- Basket Work Space Card (page 179), 1 per student
- paper
- pencils

✎ Activity

Have students place seven ants on the picnic basket and recite the equation "Seven take away zero equals seven." Write the equation on the chalkboard and have students copy it on their paper. Continue in this fashion, modeling both vertical and horizontal notation, until all the equations for 7 have been covered.

On another day, have students work independently to build and write subtraction equations for 8. Circulate as students work, offering support to those who need it. Collect the papers for evaluation. On subsequent days have students work independently with the ant manipulatives and record the corresponding number sentences for 9 and 10.

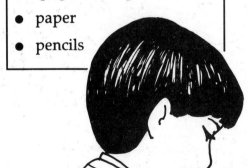

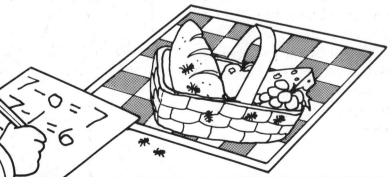

Camping Subtraction

Materials

- 5" x 7" index cards or construction paper, 1 per student
- assorted counters (beans, pebbles, etc.)

✎ Activity

Give each student an index card and some counters. Have students fold the card in half and stand it up like a tent. Ask them to use a specific number of counters (campers) to depict story problems such as the following: "Start with five campers. Put two in the tent. Now how many do you have?" Ask students to verbalize the number sentence and then proceed with other subtraction combinations. Students can also work in pairs or small groups after the activity has been modeled.

Domino Subtraction

Materials

- dominos or Domino Dot Cards (page 174)
- transparency of Domino Dot Cards (page 174)
- scissors
- overhead projector
- Domino Dots Recording Sheet (page 175), 1 per student
- pencils

✎ Activity

Cut apart the domino cards on the transparency of page 174. Display one "domino" on the overhead projector. Use a finger to cover one set of dots and verbalize the appropriate subtraction equation. For example, if the domino has a set of four dots and a set of three dots, the equation would be "seven minus three equals four" or "seven minus four equals three." Next, model how to write the equation. Repeat the activity with other dominos. Then give each student a few dominos and a Domino Dots Recording Sheet. Students are to record their dominos and the corresponding subtraction equations as shown above.

Recording Subtraction

Materials
- Subtraction Recording Sheet (page 180), 1–2 per student
- manipulatives

✎ Activity

Have the children place a selected number of objects (for example, 9) in the box at the top of the recording sheet. They write the corresponding number sentence in the first space on the page (9 - 0 = 9). Then they move one object into the "take away wagon" and write the new equation (9 - 1 = 8), continuing until all number sentences for 9 have been written. Place this activity at a center so children can practice subtraction facts. Pairs of students can take turns building and recording the problems.

3-D Subtraction Problems

Materials
- manipulatives (toothpicks, assorted beans, assorted macaroni shapes, pebbles, Styrofoam packing pieces)
- 9" x 12" construction paper or tagboard, 1 per student
- glue
- crayons or markers

✎ Activity

Have students fold the paper in four sections and write one subtraction equation in each section. Then they glue on real objects to depict the equations as shown. For example, they glue on 5 pieces of macaroni and then circle 2 of them for the equation 5 - 2 = 3. Put this activity at a center and watch students create an endless variety of 3-D equations.

Sorting Pennies for Subtraction

Materials
- pennies, number selected by teacher
- paper plates, 1 per student
- paper
- pencils

✎ Activity

Give each child a selected number of pennies and a paper plate. Have students gently shake up their pennies and place them on the paper plate. Students can form subtraction sentences by counting the total number of pennies and subtracting the number of pennies that show "heads." They can then record the resulting subtraction equation by drawing the total number of pennies and then crossing out the number subtracted.

A Very Hungry Caterpillar

Materials
- book, *The Very Hungry Caterpillar* by Eric Carle
- Caterpillar and Leaf Patterns (page 181), 1 per student
- scissors
- crayons
- scotch tape
- beans

✎ Activity

Read and discuss *The Very Hungry Caterpillar* by Eric Carle. Then have students color and cut out the caterpillar and leaf patterns. The caterpillar should be folded and taped to form an envelope. Have students work in pairs. One student tells a subtraction story problem. ("There were six beans and the caterpillar ate two, but he was still hungry. How many beans are left?") The other student places the caterpillar food on the leaf, then lets the caterpillar "eat" the amount to be subtracted. Have partners switch roles.

Hands-On Math K–1 Creative Teaching Press, Inc.

Chapter 10

Place Value

10 Place Value

1,000
100
10
1

Knowledge of our base ten number system develops gradually and builds upon previous counting knowledge. To understand place value, students need many experiences counting, grouping, and trading concrete objects to form tens and ones. They should begin by grouping single items, such as putting beans into cups or linking cubes into groups of 10. Verbalization should accompany the process ("2 tens and 3 ones"). Later you can introduce manipulatives, such as beansticks or Base Ten Blocks, that are fixed in groups of 10.

Where's My Place?—Bulletin Board

Prepare the background for the bulletin board as shown. Give students pre-cut pieces (1" x 1", 1" x 10", 10" x 10") for the place value people. They can glue on scraps for arms and legs and draw a face with a marker. Scatter the place value people around the bulletin board. Don't forget to ask each child if his or her character belongs in the hundreds, tens, or ones place!

Skills

- Group objects by tens and ones
- Record tens and ones
- Read numbers to 99
- Write numbers to 99

Learning Center

Provide a variety of materials so students can explore place value independently. Commercial materials such as Base Ten Blocks, Cuisenaire® Rods, or plastic linking cubes are excellent. Or involve students in making place value learning aids from inexpensive materials such as those shown below. Add a hundreds chart, laminated Place Value Mats (page 182), number cards 0–100, Place Value Strip Charts (pages 183 and 184), math collections, and counting cups.

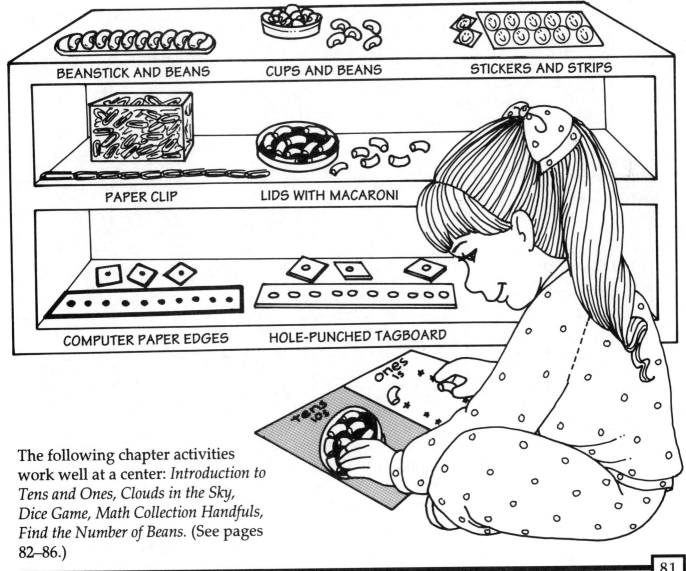

BEANSTICK AND BEANS   CUPS AND BEANS   STICKERS AND STRIPS

PAPER CLIP   LIDS WITH MACARONI

COMPUTER PAPER EDGES   HOLE-PUNCHED TAGBOARD

The following chapter activities work well at a center: *Introduction to Tens and Ones, Clouds in the Sky, Dice Game, Math Collection Handfuls, Find the Number of Beans.* (See pages 82–86.)

Activities

Introduction to Tens and Ones

Materials

- beans
- small counting cups, 9 per student
- Place Value Mats (page 182), 1 per student

✎ Activity

Provide students with the materials. Ask them to place one bean on the ones side of the Place Value Mat. Guide them in pointing to the mat and reciting, "0 tens and 1." Have them add a bean and say "0 tens and 2." Continue in this fashion until they have 10 ones. Show them how to place the 10 beans in a counting cup and move it to the tens column ("1 ten and 0"). Continue adding beans one by one and verbalizing the resulting number.

After several days, challenge students to start with a given number (24, for example) and to continue building one by one from that number. Some children will enjoy doing this as an independent activity at a learning center.

Clouds in the Sky

Materials

- large self-sealing plastic bag
- cotton balls
- 2 pieces construction paper (12" x 18")
- sandwich-size self-sealing plastic bags

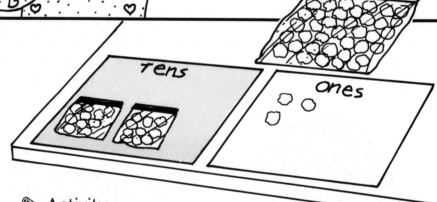

✎ Activity

Label the pieces of paper (sky) as shown. Fill the large bag with cotton balls (clouds). Place all materials at a center. Encourage students to estimate how many cotton balls are in the bag, then check their estimate by grouping the cotton balls into sets of 10. Each set of 10 is placed in a small bag. Every few days, change the number of cotton balls in the large bag and see if students can refine their estimation skills.

Read and Count

Materials

- book, *Popcorn* by Frank Asch
- large bowl or bag of popped popcorn
- small paper bags, bowls, or cups, 1 per student
- napkins, 1 per student

✎ Activity

Read to the class about Sam Bear's "popcorn party." Then have a popcorn party of your own. Give each student a small bag of popcorn, and ask each one to count the kernels by tens and ones. If you want, find the total number of kernels for the whole class. Then eat all the popcorn, just like Sam Bear's guests!

Dice Game

Materials

- plastic linking cubes (or paper clips)
- Place Value Mats (page 182), 1 per pair
- dice, 1 per pair
- timer

✎ Activity

Have each student choose a partner. Give each pair of students a Place Value Mat, one die, and some linking cubes. (Partners can take turns rolling the die.) Set the timer for five minutes. One child rolls the die and places the corresponding number of cubes on the ones side of the Place Value Mat. On subsequent rolls, students should group the cubes into sets of 10. Each group of 10 is snapped together and placed on the tens side of the mat. When the bell rings, partners tell each other how many cubes are on the mat. ("We have 2 tens and 8 ones, 28 cubes.")

Rote Counting With the Place Value Chart

Materials
- Place Value Strip Charts (pages 183 and 184), 1 per student
- scissors
- crayons

✎ Activity

Reproduce pages 183 and 184 on heavy paper or tagboard. Have the children follow the directions on the reproducible pages. Ask them to arrange the strips so zeros show in both windows. Lead students as they move the strips to correspond with their counting. Slow down as you get to 10 and ask students how they will show 10 if the strips only go to 9. Accept their responses. The counting continues to 99, using a similar procedure as each ten is reached. After the activity has been modeled for the whole group, students can work together in pairs.

Manipulatives and the Place Value Chart

Materials
- beans
- counting cups
- Place Value Strip Charts (pages 183 and 184), 1 per student

✎ Activity

This activity moves students from the mechanical adjustment of their strip charts toward the physical representation of the numbers formed. Have students take a handful of beans and count out 10 into each of the cups until all of the beans have been counted. The extras are not put into a cup, but are recorded in the ones column on the strip chart. The number of cups is recorded in the tens column.

Repeat the activity varying the number of manipulatives. (Try two or three handfuls, or try a different size bean. Also try a variety of manipulatives, such as seeds and cups, linking cubes, or paper clips.) On subsequent days, pick a number at random and ask students to build the number with manipulatives and show it on their Place Value Strip Charts.

Grouping Sets of Ten

Materials
- Place Value Mats (page 182), 1 per student
- beans or other manipulatives
- counting cups
- Place Value Recording Sheets (page 185), 1 per student
- pencils

✎ Activity

Write a number on the chalkboard. Then ask students to show that number using the beans, counting cups, and the Place Value Mats as described in the previous activity. Ask them to verbalize the number as they point to the manipulatives. For example, "17 is 1 ten and 7 ones." Next, have students write the number on the Place Value Recording Sheet.

Math Collection Handfuls

Materials
- math collections (See pages 8 and 9.)
- Work Space Cards (pages 176–178), 1 per student
- small cups for grouping tens
- Place Value Recording Sheets (page 185), 1 per student
- pencils

✎ Activity

Have students work in groups of three or four. Each child needs a set of objects from the math collections, a Work Space Card, several small cups, a Place Value Recording Sheet, and a pencil. On a signal, students grab a handful of objects from their math collection and lay the manipulatives on their Work Space Card. Next, they count the manipulatives into groups of 10 and place these in a cup. When all of the children in the group are done, they can say aloud the total number. For example, "2 tens and 7 ones is 27 buttons."

After students are comfortable with this activity, they can move to recording activities by writing the numbers on the Place Value Recording Sheet.

Trading for Tens

Materials

- Place Value Mats (page 182), 1 per student
- beans
- beansticks or other manipulatives with fixed groups of 10 (See page 81.)

✎ Activity

In preparation, let students make beansticks at a center. Use small beans, white glue, and craft sticks or tongue depressors. Allow the beansticks to dry completely.

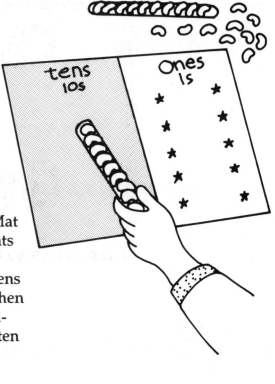

Working with a small group, give each child a Place Value Mat and some beans. (Keep the beansticks on hand.) Lead students in adding beans, one at a time, to the ones side of their Place Value Mat. Have them verbalize the number as they go: "0 tens and 1," "0 tens and 2," and so on until you reach 10 beans. Then let each child trade in 10 beans for a beanstick. Continue adding beans and counting out loud "1 ten and 0, 1 ten and 1, 1 ten and 2 . . . ." On another day try the same activity, counting backward until you reach "0 tens and 0."

Find the Number of Beans

Materials

- lids with macaroni or other manipulatives in fixed groups of 10 (See page 81.)
- Place Value Mats, 1 per student (page 182)
- overhead transparency of Place Value Mat (page 182)
- Place Value Strip Charts (pages 183 and 184) or Place Value Recording Sheets (page 185), 1 per student

✎ Activity

A few days before the activity have students prepare the manipulatives by gluing 10 pieces of macaroni in each lid. Project the Place Value Mat on the screen. Place some of the lids and individual pieces of macaroni on the tens and ones sections. Have the children duplicate the set on their own Place Value Mats. Next, they make the appropriate two-digit numeral on their strip charts or recording sheets. Display a different set on the screen and continue as described above. When students are comfortable with this activity, challenge them to build a number that is one, two, or three more (or less) than the set on the overhead projector.

Chapter 11
❦
Graphing

Graphing

Learning how to make and read graphs is an important problem-solving skill. Concrete graphs, which compare quantities of real things, are most easily understood by young children. Picture graphs use pictures to represent real things. They connect the real to the abstract and prepare children for the introduction of symbolic graphs that use symbols such as letters, numbers, lines, or bars.

K–1 students need many experiences with concrete and picture graphs. Begin with two-column graphs and model how to display the information in horizontal and vertical formats. "Reading" the graph and summarizing the information displayed is an important final step. You may even want to write up the summary in paragraph form.

Graphing Favorites—Bulletin Board

Make a graphing bulletin board that can be reused throughout the year. First, make a number of photocopies of each child's school picture and glue them on small construction paper squares. As shown above, make a graphing grid with yarn or paper strips. Place the board low enough for children to use independently. Write the graphing question and the categories on cards that can be changed periodically. For decoration, have the children add appropriate illustrations. Students answer the question by pinning their photo next to their response.

Skills

- Gather data for a graph
- Make a concrete graph
- Read a concrete graph
- Make a picture graph
- Read a picture graph
- Make a tally graph
- Read a tally graph

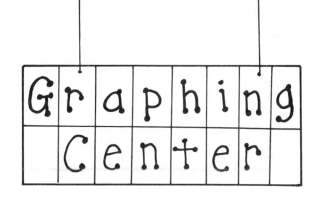

Learning Center

Center materials should encourage students to pursue graphing activities independently. Students can make concrete graphs by placing small objects in empty egg cartons, ice cube trays, or margarine tubs. For graphing larger objects, provide a floor graph. (See page 90 for directions.) Make appropriate graphing questions, such as those shown below, to go with the objects.

For pictorial graphs, students can draw original pictures or use rubber stamps, stickers, cutouts, or stencils. The blank graphing grid (page 186) can be used for pictorial or symbolic graphs. The following chapter activities would be appropriate for the graphing center: *Cereal Graph, Graphing Yummies, Raisins in Your Box,* and *Toss and Tally.* (See pages 90–94.)

Activities

Cereal Graph

Materials
- empty cereal boxes

✎ Activity

Have students bring in empty cereal boxes
to use for graphing. Select two categories, such as
sweetened and non-sweetened, and have students
sort the boxes, placing them in parallel rows on the floor. After
discussing the results, ask students to think of other categories
for graphing the cereals. (Example: hot/cold cereal, favorite kind
of cereal, size of box, type of grain.) Place a list of their ideas at a
center, and let students work independently to graph the boxes
in a variety of ways.

Favorite Color Graph

Materials
- large floor graph
- crayons
- question card
- label cards

✎ Activity

Purchase a floor graph. Or, make a graphing grid on a long
rectangular vinyl tablecloth or a plastic shower curtain. Use
a permanent marking pen or strips of colored cloth tape to
make the lines.

Prepare a question card
(Example: What is your
favorite color?) and 4 to
6 label cards (red, blue,
yellow, green, etc.).
Have the children
select their favorite
color crayon and gather
round the floor graph.
Ask students who
chose red crayons to
place them, one in each
box, in the first row.
This process is repeated
until all of the children
have participated.

Graphing Yummies

Materials

- snack mix or trail mix
- Graph Recording Sheets (page 186) or 5" x 7" index cards, 1 per student
- glue

✏️ Activity

Give each child a Graph Recording Sheet and a handful of the snack mix. Then have students sort the snack mix on the recording sheet and glue on the food items. While waiting for the glue to dry, give each child another handful of snack mix for munching. Encourage each child to tell the class about his or her graph.

Raisins in Your Box

Materials

- small boxes of raisins, 1 per student
- large paper for graph grid, at least 24" x 36"
- glue

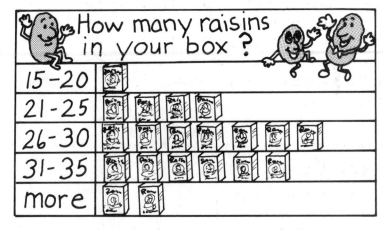

✏️ Activity

Prepare a graph grid as shown. Then give each child a box of raisins. Have students count the number of raisins in their box and glue the box on the graph in the appropriate row. Discuss the results as students snack on their raisins.

Stackable Graphables

Materials

- milk cartons (uniform size), 1 per student
- scissors
- oil-based marking pen
- individually wrapped hard candies in several different flavors

✏️ Activity

Cut off the bottom 2" of each milk carton to use for this activity. Write a child's name on each carton. (These can be used to hold small objects for a variety of graphing activities.) Let each child pick a favorite flavor of candy and place it in the carton. Then have students stack the cartons by flavor. Or arrange them in horizontal rows.

Favorite Book Graph

Materials
- two books by the same author
- 5" x 7" index cards, 1 per student
- crayons
- chart paper
- glue

✎ Activity
Read the two books to the class, or use books students are already familiar with. Put the books on the floor or on a table and ask the class "Which book did you like best?" Have students line up behind the book they prefer. Count and discuss the resulting people graph.

Then have students fold an index card and draw their favorite book cover on the front. Glue these cards on chart paper to make a pictorial graph.

Gumball Graph

Materials
- paper graph grid, at least 24" x 36"
- white self-stick circles (or white paper circles and glue), 1 per student
- gumballs, 1 per student

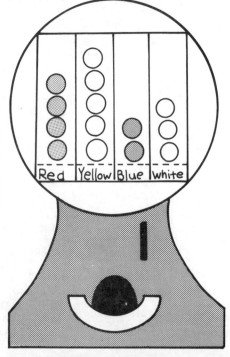

✎ Activity
Give each child one circle sticker and one gumball. Have students color the white circle to match their gumball color. As a group, decide how many different colors there are. Then model how to divide the paper into the appropriate number of sections, and label each section with a color word. Next, have students place their gumball stickers in the appropriate row or column.

Favorite Character Graph

Materials

- 2 or 3 favorite storybooks
- large sheet of butcher paper
- marker
- 3" x 3" sticky notes
- crayons

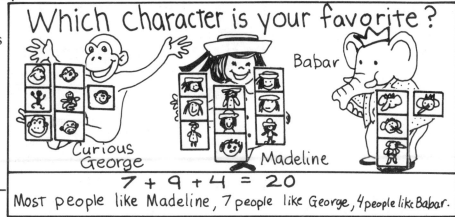

Which character is your favorite?

Babar

Curious George

Madeline

7 + 9 + 4 = 20

Most people like Madeline, 7 people like George, 4 people like Babar.

✎ Activity

Children should be very familiar with the chosen books. On the butcher paper, draw a simple outline of the main character from each book. Add the title "Which Character Is Your Favorite?" Have students draw a picture of their favorite character on a sticky note and place it on the graph. As a group, write a summary of the results.

Favorite Playground Activity

Materials

- paper graph grid, at least 24" x 36"
- 3" x 3" paper squares, 1 per student
- glue sticks
- crayons

✎ Activity

Prepare the graph grid as shown. Then ask students to draw a self-portrait on the paper square and glue the square on the graph next to their favorite playground activity.

How Many Beds?

Materials

- paper graph grid, at least 24" x 36"
- cotton ball, 1 per student
- glue

✎ Activity

Prepare a graph grid, as shown, with the following title: "How many beds do you have at home?" Then have students stretch a cotton ball into a pillow shape and glue it on the graph in the appropriate column/row.

How many beds?

1 2 3 4 5 6 or more

Count the Letters in Your Name

Materials
- clothespins, 1 per student
- marker
- strips of tagboard
- index cards
- stapler

3	4	5	6	7 or more
Ron	Lucy	Maria	Steven	Michael
Ted	Beth	Alice	Shauna	Garrett
Kim	José	Janet	Kendra	Christopher
	Yuri	Brian		Brandon
	Evan			

✎ Activity
Staple one strip of tagboard on each index card as shown. Write numbers on the index cards to represent the number of letters in a name. Pin these cards securely to a bulletin board. Then give each child a clothespin with his or her first name printed on it. Have students count the number of letters in their name and clip their clothespin onto the corresponding number strip to create a vertical graph. Save the clothespins to use for other graphing activities.

Tally Graph

Materials
- 24" x 36" piece of paper
- thick-line marking pen

How many people are in my family?

	2	3	
	I	⊔⊔⊤⊤	
4	5	6	7 or more
⊔⊔⊤⊤ I	II		

✎ Activity
Divide the paper into six sections with the following headings: 2, 3, 4, 5, 6, 7 or more. Ask students how many people are in their family. Have them come up one by one and place one tally mark under the appropriate number.

Toss and Tally

Materials
- dice or number cubes, 1 per student
- 5" x 7" index cards, 1 per student
- pencils

✎ Activity
Help students divide their card into six equal sections, and have them write one numeral in each section (1–6). Students roll the number cube and record the number shown by making a tally mark under the corresponding numeral. Set a limit of 20 tosses. Let students repeat the activity and compare the results.

Chapter 12
❧ Estimation

Estimation

One of the most important concepts that children learn through estimation activities is that it is not always necessary to find one "exact" or "correct" answer. An estimated answer is often good enough. Estimation also develops students' ability to recognize when numbers are reasonable and make sense. The activities in this chapter provide estimating practice in several mathematical areas: quantity, weight, temperature, time, length, capacity, and numerical approximation.

Take a Good Guess—Bulletin Board

Cut large paper shapes for the gumball machine. Add about 50 colorful circles for gumballs, being sure to overlap some of them. Post a "Gumball Guess" recording sheet, and ask each child to record his or her estimate of the number of gumballs in the machine. On a designated day, have the class count the gumballs together as the paper circles are removed from the bulletin board.

Use a similar estimation board throughout the year by changing the theme: apples on a tree; pumpkins in a patch; birds in a tree; insects in the grass; or a jar filled with objects like pennies, jelly beans, pickles, or cherries. Have students draw and cut out illustrations for the board.

Skills

- Estimate quantity
- Estimate capacity
- Estimate weight
- Estimate length/height
- Estimate temperature
- Estimate time
- Recognize when numbers are reasonable and make sense

Learning Center

After modeling a variety of estimation activities, such as those described on pages 98–102, let students explore similar activities at a learning center. Provide copies of the Guess and Count Cards (page 187) so children can record their experiences. Encourage repeated investigations with the same type of material; for example, investigating capacity by using rice to fill a variety of containers. With each repetition, estimates should become more accurate. Below is a list of materials that are useful for independent estimation activities:

▲ **Capacity**
variety of containers
rice, birdseed, beans
scoops
measuring cups

▲ **Quantity**
variety of containers
small objects to fill containers

▲ **Length**
string
scissors
objects to measure

▲ **Weight**
balance scale
digital bathroom scale
objects to weigh
Estimating Weight Cards (page 188)

▲ **Time**
stopwatch
timer
Estimating Time Cards (page 189)

The following chapter activities can also be placed at the center: *Estimation Jar, How Much Does It Hold?, My Own String, Guess How Heavy, How Much Does It Weigh?, Estimating Handfuls.* (See pages 98–102.)

Activities

Estimation Jar

Materials
- clear jar with lid
- objects to put in jar: candy corn, jelly beans, goldfish crackers, marbles, pebbles, paper clips, pennies
- basket or box

 Activity

Each week fill the jar with a different object. Start with a few large items, such as marshmallows or walnuts in the shell, and progress to smaller items, such as jelly beans or M & M's®. Begin with 0–30 items for kindergarten and 0–100 items for first grade. You don't always have to fill the jar to the top.

Invite each student to look closely at the jar and guess how many objects are in it. Help students record their guess on a piece of paper and drop the paper in a basket near the estimation jar. At the end of the week, have the whole class count the objects in the jar. (You may want to use the paper squares to graph the guesses.) Ask the class how the following factors influence their guesses: the size of the objects, the size of the jar, the shape of the jar, and how full the jar is.

Feeling the Water

Materials
- 2–3 transparent containers
- thermometer

 Activity

Fill two containers with water of different temperatures (Be sure the "hot" water is not too hot.) Have several volunteers feel the outsides of the jars and try to determine which jar holds the warmest water. Then use the thermometer to measure the actual temperature of the two samples. Repeat this activity using three containers of water of varying temperatures. Use the thermometer to check students' guesses.

How Much Does It Hold?

Materials
- transparent jars of varying sizes and shapes
- masking tape
- marker
- 2–3 lbs. rice or birdseed
- 1/4 or 1/2 cup measure
- Guess and Count Cards (page 187)

✎ Activity

Fill a tub with rice. Label each jar with a different letter. Place all of the materials at a center and let students use the measuring cups to fill the containers. Then gather the class together and display one jar. Ask students to guess how many scoops it will take to fill the jar. Have students record their guesses on the Guess and Count Cards. Invite one student to fill the jar as the whole class counts the scoops. Students should compare their estimates with the actual count. Have the children follow the same procedure for the other jars as they work independently at the center.

How Tall/Long?

Materials
- string
- scissors
- chart paper
- tape

✎ Activity

Choose a person or an object in the room that students can use to estimate height/length. Ask the class, "How long should this string be to equal the length of the desk?" Let each child cut a piece of string and then compare it with the chosen object. Then hang the strings on the chart paper under the appropriate heading: Too Short, Too Long, Just Right.

My Own String

Materials

- pieces of string of various lengths, 1 per student
- paper or recording sheet
- pencils

 Activity

Give each child a piece of string to examine. While remaining in their seats, students look around the room for something that is approximately the same length as their string. When a signal is given by the teacher, each student checks his estimate by placing his string next to his chosen object. If correct, he sits down and records his findings, either by writing the name of the object or by drawing a picture of it. If his guess was incorrect, he tries different objects until he finds one that matches the length of his string. The strings can be redistributed for another round of this activity or placed at a center for independent investigations.

Guess How Heavy

Materials

- Estimating Weight Cards (page 188), 1 set
- objects to weigh (must match Estimating Weight Cards)
- balance scale

Activity

Reproduce the Estimating Weight Cards on heavy paper or tagboard, cut them apart, and laminate them. Place all of the materials at a center. Students select a picture card, find the matching objects, and estimate which object weighs more by holding one object in each hand. Next, they weigh the objects on the balance scale to verify their estimate.

How Much Does It Weigh?

Materials

- digital bathroom scale or kitchen scale
- 1 lb. bag of rice or beans
- 5 lb. bag of rice or beans
- heavy objects (5 lb. bag of potatoes, large pumpkin, telephone book, canned foods)
- chart paper
- marker

✎ Activity

Pass around the bag of rice so each child can feel how heavy 1 lb. is. Then pass around a 5 lb. bag of rice and ask students to estimate the weight. Record their guesses on a chart as they whisper their estimates in your ear.

Place the bag of rice on the scale to find the actual weight. Let students follow the same procedure with other heavy objects. Encourage them to compare the weight of the other items with the known weight of the rice. For an ongoing activity, change the object each week.

Guess How Long It Takes

Materials

- plastic or wooden cubes, 1 per student
- Estimating Time Cards (page 189), 1 set
- stopwatch (optional)

✎ Activity

Reproduce the Estimating Time Cards on heavy paper or tagboard, cut them apart, and laminate them. Give each child a cube. Show two of the cards and ask the class, "Which will take longer, tying a shoe or singing the alphabet?" Lay the cards on the floor, and have students place their cube below the picture of the activity they think will take longer. Then have two students try the activities and see which takes longer. You may want to time each student with a stopwatch. Record the time for each activity on the chalkboard or on a chart.

Estimating Handfuls

Materials
- math collections (See pages 8 and 9.)
- Guess and Count Cards (page 187)
- pencils

✎ Activity

Each child takes a handful of manipulatives from a math collection, estimates the number of objects, and writes his or her guess on a Guess and Count Card. (There is a space where students can draw a picture of the object.) Then the student counts the objects and records the number on the "count" side of the card. Have students try the game two or three times with the same material, then change materials and repeat the procedure.

Estimation With Literature

Materials
- book, *Pumpkin, Pumpkin* by Jeanne Titherington
- pumpkin
- knife
- big spoon
- paper towels
- counting cups
- bathroom scale
- string
- scissors
- chart paper

✎ Activity

After reading *Pumpkin, Pumpkin* to the class, use a real pumpkin for a variety of estimation activities. Have students estimate the number of vertical lines on the pumpkin. Then count the actual number together. Ask students to estimate the weight and then verify their guess using a bathroom scale.

Students can estimate the pumpkin's circumference by cutting a piece of string they think would fit around the middle. After they measure, they hang the string on a chart under the following labels: Too Short, Just Right, Too Long. Finally, carve the pumpkin and let the children peek inside to estimate how many seeds there are. Have students take turns scooping out the seeds and counting them into small cups by tens to verify their estimates.

Chapter 13

Time

13

Time

The activities in this chapter will help young children develop an awareness of time by focusing on sequencing of events and duration of time. Students are also introduced to telling time by the hour and half hour, using both digital and standard clocks.

Times of the Day—Bulletin Board

Involve students in making this bulletin board about times of the day. Attach four or five cards showing different times of the day or night. Under each card, pin student drawings of activities appropriate for that time. For younger students, post a daytime and a nighttime picture, and have students draw pictures depicting day or night activities. To concentrate on times of the year, post several calendar pages. Beneath each one, post student illustrations of activities appropriate for the month.

Skills

- Sequence events
- Estimate passage of time
- Know parts of a clock face
- Tell time to the hour
- Tell time to the half hour

Learning Center

Provide a large demonstration clock with movable hands that children can use to practice setting and reading the time. Post a chart showing clock faces and times so students can self-check their work. Set out index cards, a clock face rubber stamp, and a stamp pad so students can make their own set of flash cards to use with a partner. Include a kitchen timer, an egg timer, and a stopwatch for exploring shorter segments of time.

Gather a collection of books about time, such as *The Grouchy Ladybug* by Eric Carle or *The Guy Who Was Five Minutes Late* by Bill Grossman. (See page 220 for other titles.) Invite students to bring in old clocks or watches that can be kept at the center for exploration activities. Rummage and garage sales are an inexpensive source of such items.

The following chapter activities would also work well at a center: *Before Lunch or After Lunch, What Can You Do in Three Minutes?, Reading Time to the Hour, Writing Time to the Hour, Clock Concentration, Through-the-Day Book, Grouchy Ladybug.* (See pages 106–110.)

Activities

When Can It Happen?

Materials
● pencils
● paper
● markers/crayons

✎ Activity

Divide the class into groups of four or five students. Ask each group to think about typical daytime and nighttime activities. Then each group shares (or acts out) three of its best ideas and classmates guess if it is a daytime or a nighttime activity. Next, have students fold unlined paper into four sections and draw pictures of two daytime and two nighttime activities. They can also include a sun or moon symbol with each drawing.

Before Lunch or After Lunch?

Materials
● 2" x 5" cards or paper strips, 2 per student
● masking tape

✎ Activity

Write the headings "before lunch" and "after lunch" on the board. Give each student two cards and two pieces of tape. Students copy one heading on each card and tape the cards on objects used in morning or afternoon activities. For example, one child might tape the "before lunch" card to the piano because the class sings in the morning, and the "after lunch" card to the bookshelves because silent reading time is in the afternoon. Collect the cards and repeat the activity, or place the cards at a center for children to use independently.

What Can You Do in Three Minutes?

Materials
● egg timer
● chart paper
● marker

In 3 minutes we can...
✓ sing "Yankee Doodle" ♪
✓ write numbers 1-20
✓ get ready for recess
✓ tie shoes

✎ Activity

Start an egg timer and let students experience how long it takes the sand to run through. Discuss activities that could be completed in this space of time and write students' ideas on a chart. Then have volunteers perform each activity, resetting the egg timer for each one. Revise the list as needed. Place the egg timer at a center, and let students add to the list of activities they can perform in three minutes' time.

Which Takes Longer?

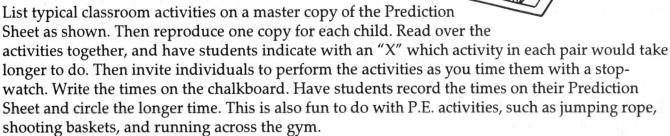

Materials
- Prediction Sheet (page 190), 1 per student
- stopwatch
- pencils

✎ Activity

List typical classroom activities on a master copy of the Prediction Sheet as shown. Then reproduce one copy for each child. Read over the activities together, and have students indicate with an "X" which activity in each pair would take longer to do. Then invite individuals to perform the activities as you time them with a stopwatch. Write the times on the chalkboard. Have students record the times on their Prediction Sheet and circle the longer time. This is also fun to do with P.E. activities, such as jumping rope, shooting baskets, and running across the gym.

Giant Clock

Materials
- playground chalk or tempera paint

✎ Activity

This game will help students develop a kinesthetic sense for the position of the numbers on a clock. Draw a giant clock on the playground. Have two or three students stand on each number. Ask one child to stand in the middle of the clock and call out two different times, such as "4 o'clock" and "11 o'clock." On that command, the children standing on 4 must change places with the children standing on 11 without being tagged by the person in the middle. Anyone who is tagged becomes "it" and must stand in the center.

Parts of a Clock Face

Materials
- demonstration clock
- Standard Clocks (page 191), 1 per student
- paper fasteners
- crayons or markers
- scissors

✎ Activity

Reproduce the student clock on tagboard. Have students color, cut out, and attach the clock hands with a paper fastener. Introduce the terms *clock face*, *hour hand*, and *minute hand* and have students touch each clock part as it is named. Next, have children work in pairs to identify the parts.

Reading Time to the Hour

Materials
- Standard Clocks (page 191), 1 per student
- demonstration clock

✎ Activity
Model how to set the clock on the hour, verbalizing how the hands are placed. ("When the hour hand is on the 4 and the minute hand is on the 12, it is 4 o'clock.") Ask the class to set their individual clocks following your example. When students seem to have a good understanding, have them work with a partner. One child sets the clock, and his or her partner reads the time. This same activity can be used for telling time to the half hour.

Writing Time to the Hour

Materials
- Standard Clocks (page 191), 1 per student
- demonstration clock
- paper
- pencils

✎ Activity
Ask students to set their clocks at 9 o'clock. Then demonstrate on the chalkboard how to write the time (9:00, 9 o'clock). Have students fold a piece of paper in eight parts. Each time you say a time, they should set their clock to the time and write the time in one box on the paper. Later, partners can take turns setting the clock and writing the time on the back of the paper. This activity can also be used for writing time to the half hour.

One Hour Later/Earlier

Materials
- Standard Clocks (page 191) or Digital Clocks (page 192), 1 per student
- chalk
- chalkboard

✎ Activity
Write a time on the board. Ask students to read it and make their clocks show "one hour later or earlier" than the time written on the board. Repeat the activity, letting volunteers write the time on the board.

Hands-On Math K–1

Matching Times

Materials
- Digital Clocks (page 192), 1 per student
- Standard Clocks (page 191), 1 each for half the students
- demonstration clock (standard)
- scissors

✎ Activity

Have students cut out and assemble the digital clock following the directions on page 192. Set the demonstration clock on the hour, and ask students to set their digital clocks for exactly the same time. Repeat the activity with different times (hour and half hour).

On another day, provide half the class with standard clocks and the other half with digital clocks. Ask students to set their clocks on the hour (or half hour) of their choice. On a signal from the teacher, students with digital clocks try to find a matching standard clock. Let students without a match, reset their clocks to make a match.

Clock Concentration

Materials
- Standard Clock Faces (page 193), 1 set
- Digital Clock Faces (page 194), 1 set
- 24 index cards
- fine-line marker
- glue
- scissors

✎ Activity

Using a copy of page 193, draw hands on the blank clocks so each clock shows a different hour. Write in matching times on the digital clocks on page 194. Cut the clocks apart and glue them on index cards. Players spread all the cards face down on the floor. Then they turn over two cards at a time trying to find a matching pair. The player who finds a match keeps it and takes another turn. The goal is to collect the most matching clocks. As a variation, students can use the same cards to play a telling time version of "Go Fish."

It's Time for . . .

Materials
- kitchen timer
- Standard Clocks (page 191), 1 per student

✎ Activity
As you go about your day-to-day classroom activities, set the timer to ring at important times (10:00 snack, 12:00 lunch, 1:30 music). When the timer rings, ask the class to tell you the time and to change their individual clocks to show the same time.

Through-the-Day Book

Materials
- Standard Clock Faces (page 193) or clock rubber stamp and stamp pad
- crayons
- pencils
- 9" x 12" paper
- glue

✎ Activity
Reproduce multiple copies of the clock faces on page 193. Cut them apart and give students several clocks and several pieces of paper. Have them draw in hands to show a different time on each clock and glue each clock on a separate piece of paper. Next, students illustrate and/or write about something they do at those times during the day. Assemble the pages in chronological order. Add a clock cover, and each child has a book to share with friends and family. As a variation on this activity, make a class Big Book describing times throughout the school day.

Grouchy Ladybug

Materials
- book, *The Grouchy Ladybug* by Eric Carle
- Ladybug Cards (page 195), 1 set per group

✎ Activity
After reading the story, give each group a set of Ladybug Cards. Let students take turns picking a card and reading the time on it. Then encourage each child to make up a new verse for the story. For example, if the card reads 5:00, a child might say this: At five o'clock the ladybug met a zebra. "Want to fight," asked the ladybug? The zebra kicked up his heels, and the ladybug said, "Oh, you're not big enough anyway."

Chapter 14

Measurement

Measurement

The activities in this chapter give children experiences in measuring length, mass, and capacity using non-standard and standard units of measure. Both metric and imperial systems are included, but your guidelines will dictate which to introduce to your students.

Young children need help learning how to use and read measuring tools such as rulers, scales, and measuring cups. They should be given opportunities to describe measurements that are not exact (between 5 and 6 popsicle sticks, close to one pound, about 3 inches). In addition, students should be encouraged to estimate before measuring. Each attempt will help them refine later estimates.

How Long/Tall Is It?—Bulletin Board

Attach a tall giraffe cutout to a colorful background. Cut out a number of simple objects, such as those pictured above, and post them on the bulletin board. Place several rulers and non-standard units of measure (blocks, strips of paper, pencils, sticks) nearby. Encourage students to measure the different items on the board with a variety of measuring tools. Students can record their estimates and measurements on the Measurement Recording Sheet (page 196).

Skills

■ Compare length, mass, and capacity of objects

■ Estimate and measure length, mass, and capacity in non-standard units

■ Estimate and measure length in standard units (inches/centimeters, yards/meters)

■ Estimate and measure capacity in standard units (cup, pint, quart, liter)

■ Estimate and measure mass in standard units (pounds, ounces/grams)

Learning Center

Children need many opportunities to explore measurement using a wide variety of standard and non-standard units of measure. Set up a center where students can work independently to make new discoveries and to confirm previous learnings. Students can use the following materials for measuring length, mass, and capacity:

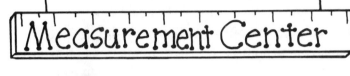

▲ non-standard units for measurement (strings, blocks, paper strips, straws, etc.)

▲ objects of different lengths

▲ assortment of curved objects to be measured with strings

▲ inch and centimeter rulers

▲ yardstick/meter stick

▲ cloth and/or metal tape measures

▲ balance scale

▲ bathroom, kitchen, and postal scales

▲ assorted objects to weigh

▲ measuring cups and spoons

▲ pint, quart, and liter containers

▲ tub of rice

The following chapter activities on pages 114–118 would work well at a learning center: *Find Something As Long As This, Make a Row As Long As This, Make a Tower As Tall As This, Measuring With String, Longer or Shorter?, Measuring Rice, Count and Fill, Which Is Heavier?, Count and Balance, Comparing Weights.*

Activities

Find Something As Long As This

Materials
- pieces of string, assorted lengths (2"–20"), 1 per student

✎ Activity
Give each child a piece of string. Model how to measure length correctly by matching the end of the string with the edge of an object. Then ask students to find an object in the classroom that is about the same length as their string. Let each child share his or her match with the rest of the class. Have children exchange strings and repeat the activity. Or, place the strings at a center for independent exploration.

Make a Row As Long As This

Materials
- math collections (See pages 8 and 9.)
- 18" x 24" construction paper, 1 per student
- file folders, 1 per pair
- cubes (optional)

✎ Activity
Divide the class into groups of two. Give each child a piece of construction paper and a handful of manipulatives. (Partners should have the same kind of manipulative.) One child places some objects in a row on his paper. The other child tries to make a row that is the same length on her paper. Next, students determine whether their rows are equal in length by lining them up side by side.

Extend this activity, by placing a partition between the partners after the initial look. Then students must rely on visual memory to make a row the same length. The partition is removed when it's time to compare the rows. Students can focus on height by doing this activity using wooden cubes to build towers.

Make a Tower As Tall As This

Materials
- plastic linking cubes, 20–30 per group
- slips of paper
- hat or box
- pencils

 Activity

Write the names (or draw pictures) of classroom objects on the slips of paper. Place the papers in a hat or box. Divide the children into groups of three or four. Give each group the linking cubes. (Students can use building blocks to measure larger objects.) Have each group draw a slip of paper from the box, find the object shown, and make a tower as tall as the object. Encourage students to estimate before they measure and to record the estimate and the actual measurement on the slip of paper. Let children try measuring a number of different objects.

Measuring With String

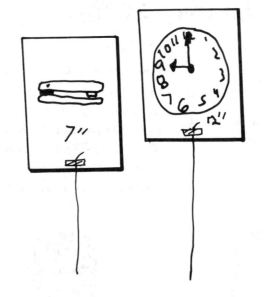

Materials
- string
- scissors
- index cards, 1 per student
- tape
- pencils
- ruler/yardstick/meter stick (optional)

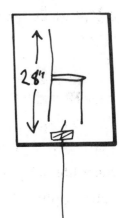

 Activity

Give each child a piece of string and an index card. Have students find an object in the classroom, measure it with the string, and cut the string the same length as the object. Next, they draw a picture of the object on the index card and tape the string to the card. Display these on the wall, or place them at the measuring center for other children to use. Classmates can confirm the measurements or find other objects about the same length. They can also use a ruler, yardstick, or meter stick to measure the strings.

Longer or Shorter?

Materials
- objects to measure
- inch/centimeter ruler
- crayons
- large drawing paper
- 2 hoops or circles of yarn for Venn diagram
- 3 labels ("shorter," "same," "longer")

✎ Activity

Place all of the materials at a center. Students compare the objects with the length of the ruler. Shorter objects are placed on the left of the Venn diagram. Longer objects go on the right, and objects that are the same length go in the center. Encourage students to record their findings by drawing a picture of their Venn diagram on a large sheet of drawing paper and recording the length of each object.

As an extension of this activity, students can search the room for different objects to compare with a ruler or a yardstick. These findings can also be recorded on drawing paper.

Using Rulers

Materials
- book, *Inch by Inch* by Leo Lionni
- Inch or Centimeter Rulers (page 197), 1 per pair
- paper
- pencils
- crayons
- scissors

✎ Activity

Introduce this activity by reading about the inch-worm that measured the birds in *Inch by Inch* by Leo Lionni. Reproduce the inch or centimeter ruler on page 197 on heavy paper or tagboard. Ask students to color and cut out the ruler. (Model how to use the ruler.) Have students work with a partner to measure three or four classroom objects. On another day, have partners compare measurements of an object using an inch ruler and a centimeter ruler.

Measuring Rice

Materials

- uncooked rice, several pounds
- plastic dishpan or tub
- widemouthed containers, various sizes and shapes
- measuring cups
- pint, quart/liter jars
- drop cloth or sheet

✎ Activity

This activity is best done in small groups or at a center. Let children discover the capacity of a variety of containers. Students use rice and measuring cups to fill the containers, counting the cups as they work. For easy cleanup, place a large bed sheet or a paint cloth on the floor. Pick up the cloth with the rice inside, and pour the rice back into the tub.

Count and Fill

Materials

- 3–4 widemouthed containers, various sizes and shapes
- pint, quart/liter jars
- non-standard unit of measure (scoop, paper cup)
- plastic counters
- tub with rice
- drop cloth
- Measurement Recording Sheet (page 196)
- pencils

✎ Activity

Number the containers and place all of the materials at a center. Ask pairs of students to estimate how many scoops of rice the #1 container will hold and write the estimate on the Measurement Recording Sheet. To check their guess, one student fills the container. His or her partner keeps a record by placing a counter next to the container each time a scoop is added. When students have made and checked each estimate, they place the containers in order from the smallest to the largest in capacity.

Which Is Heavier?

Materials

- balance scale, 1 per group
- assortment of objects to weigh
- pencils
- paper

✎ Activity

This activity can be done by small groups or placed at a center. Students select two objects to weigh, hold both objects to estimate which is heavier, and record their guess. They can confirm their guess by weighing both objects on a balance scale.

Count and Balance

Materials

- balance scale
- collection of objects to weigh
- non-standard units for weighing (clothespins, linking cubes, craft sticks, paper clips)
- Measurement Recording Sheet (page 196)
- pencils

✎ Activity

This activity works best at a center or with small groups. Have students place an object on the scale and balance the scale by putting non-standard units of measure, such as clothespins, on the other side. Ask one student to count how many clothespins it took to balance the object. Based on this experience, students see if they can estimate how many clothespins would be needed to balance a different object. Students can use the Measurement Recording Sheet to record their work.

Comparing Weights

Materials

- kitchen scale
- objects to weigh (apple, can of soup, soap, block, scissors, box of crayons)
- paper or Measurement Recording Sheet (page 196)
- pencils/crayons

✎ Activity

Place all of the materials at a center. Encourage students to practice weighing various objects on the kitchen scale. They will enjoy estimating how much each item weighs and then finding the actual weight. Students can also draw pictures of the objects and record how much they weigh.

Chapter 15

Money

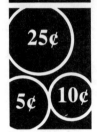
Money

The purpose of this chapter is two fold, to familiarize students with coins and their relative values and to give them experience using money. Although coin identities and values are learned primarily through rote memorization, children benefit most from actual experiences with money transactions. When possible, use real coins for the chapter activities. This will ensure greater transfer to real-life experiences with money.

What's For Lunch?—Bulletin Board

Display pictures of lunch foods on the board. These pictures can be cut from magazines, or drawn by students. Label each food item with a price (1¢, 5¢, 10¢, 25¢). Enlarge the coins on reproducible page 202, and place an assortment of them in a self-sealing plastic bag that is stapled to the bulletin board. Let students choose what they want for lunch and "pay" for it by hanging (or pinning) the matching coins next to the chosen food items.

Skills

- Identify penny, nickel, dime, quarter
- Learn value of penny, nickel, dime, quarter
- Count coins

Learning Center

Set up a classroom store so students can practice using money for authentic purposes. Make this an ongoing center by changing the type of products for sale. Possibilities are a clothing store, grocery store, bookstore, card shop, sporting goods store, toy store, or department store. Children can price the products, role-play cashier or customer, and use real or play money to make purchases. A list of materials follows:

- ▲ real objects to "sell"
- ▲ price tags
- ▲ posters and signs for advertising sales

- ▲ real or play money
- ▲ cash box or register
- ▲ calculator or pencil and paper for totaling purchases

The following chapter activities would also work well at a center: *Buying Clothes, Literature Activity, All Aboard, Trading Coins, Coupon Game, Restaurant.* (See pages 122–126.)

Activities

In preparation for these money activities, prepare a set of coins for each student. You can use real coins, commercial plastic coins, or the tagboard coins on reproducible page 202. Store them in small self-sealing plastic bags, each labeled with a child's name.

Readiness for Money—Switch Counting

Materials
● none

✎ Activity

To count money with ease, students need to know how to count by ones, fives, and tens interchangeably. To practice switch counting, have students count by tens. When the teacher holds up five fingers, the counting switches from counting by tens to counting by fives. For example, "10, 20, 30, (five fingers held up) 35, 40, 45 . . . ." Be sure students feel comfortable with switch counting before proceeding with the next step.

Next, add counting by ones. Now the counting could go like this: "10, 20, 30, 40 (five fingers held up), 45, 50, 55, 60, 65 (one finger held up) 66, 67, 68 . . . ." Repeat this until a preliminary level of understanding is reached. Mastery of this type of counting is not necessary at this point. The children will gain further understanding as they repeat this type of counting while manipulating coins. (Kindergarten students may not go beyond counting pennies by ones. However, switch counting could still be a fun game to prepare them for later skills.)

Money Sorting

Materials
● coins, 1 set per student
● teacher demonstration coins

✎ Activity

Make a set of large coins for demonstration purposes. (You can enlarge the coins on reproducible page 202.) Give each child, or pair of children, an assortment of coins. Ask them to sort the coins any way they wish. Discuss the attributes used. Then show the demonstration coins pointing out the special characteristics of each coin. Have students find the corresponding coin.

Shopping With Pennies (Nickels, Dimes, Quarters)

Materials
- coins, 1 set per student
- objects with price tags

✎ Activity

Before the activity, price the objects from 1¢ to 20¢. Ask students to separate the pennies from their sets of coins and to find the total value of the pennies. Then hold up an object, such as a toy car. Ask a child to read the price tag on the car, and have students separate the number of pennies needed to make that purchase. Repeat with other objects. After modeling the activity, have students work in small groups. Let the children take turns selecting objects for the others to "buy."

On another day, repeat the activity using just nickels. Students separate the nickels in their sets of coins and find the total value of nickels by counting by fives. Price objects in multiples of five, and have students find the number of nickels needed to "buy" the item. To introduce shopping with dimes and quarters proceed as above.

For a more difficult activity, mix the coins. For example, for an item priced at 23¢, students could count out 2 dimes and 3 pennies. This involves switch counting as described on page 122.

Literature Activity

Materials
- book, *26 Letters and 99 Cents* by Tana Hoban
- large plastic self-sealing bag
- real or play money

✎ Activity

After reading the story, let students work independently o in pairs to duplicate the sets of coins shown in the book. Children will enjoy laying the real coins on top of the coins pictured on the page. Ask them to verbalize which coins were used and the total number of cents.

Buying Clothes

Materials
- Money Spinner (page 199)
- Clothing Game (page 198), 1 per student

✎ Activity

Assemble the spinner and place all materials at a center. (Or make several spinners and have students work with a partner.) Students must cut out the paper doll and the clothing items on page 198 before the game begins. Players take turns spinning the Money Spinner and "purchasing" clothing items for their paper dolls. For example, if the spinner lands on 25¢, the player may buy shoes, since shoes are priced at 25¢. Whoever dresses his or her doll first is the winner.

All Aboard

Materials
- chairs
- tickets (1¢, 5¢, 10¢, 25¢)
- real or play money

✎ Activity

This activity works well at a center. Set up the chairs in train/bus formation. (Post a sign listing destinations and fares, or let students invent their own destinations.) Students can role-play the parts of the conductor and passengers. As passengers board the train, they tell the conductor their destination and buy a ticket for the correct fare. For example: "I'm going to the zoo." "That will be 25¢, please."

Equivalent Sets With Dimes, Nickels, Pennies

Materials
- teacher demonstration coins (dime, nickel, penny)
- coins, 1 set per student
- transparency of Coins reproducible (page 202)
- overhead projector

✎ Activity

Make a set of coins for the overhead projector using reproducible page 202. Cut the coins apart. Display a nickel on the screen. Ask students to make 5¢ in another way. Repeat with a dime and then a quarter. Let students share the different ways to make 5¢, 10¢, or 25¢. As students share, display the different combinations on the overhead projector.

Continue the activity, changing the amounts each time. Let students take turns being the leader. Limits can also be imposed. For example, use only pennies or nickels, pennies and nickels but not dimes, and so on.

Trading Coins

Materials
- number cubes or dice, 1 per group
- coins, 1 set per group

✎ Activity

Have children work in groups of three or four. Students take turns rolling the die and withdrawing pennies from the "bank." As soon as a player has 5 pennies, they should be traded in for a nickel. When 2 nickels are collected, they should be traded in for a dime, and so forth. After each child has had several turns, each student finds the total value of his or her coins.

Adding Money

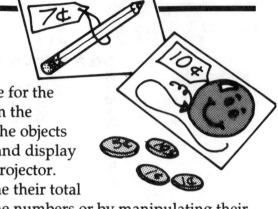

Materials

- transparencies of Things to Buy, Sets A and B (pages 200 and 201)
- overhead projector
- coins, 1 set per student
- paper
- pencils

✎ Activity

Write prices appropriate for the level of your students on the transparencies and cut the objects apart. Select two items and display them on the overhead projector. Have students determine their total cost, either by adding the numbers or by manipulating their coins. Answers are then compared. The activity is repeated, perhaps with three items. The children will discover that adding prices is just like adding numbers.

Coupon Game

Materials

- 15–20 coupons
- index cards
- glue
- real or play money (for the bank)

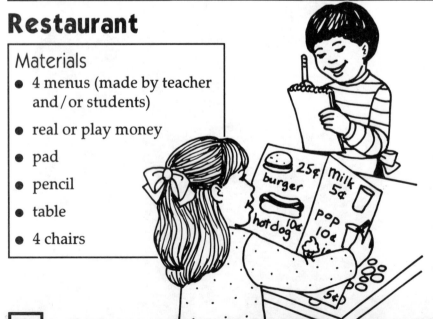

✎ Activity

Glue one coupon on each index card and place the set of cards at a center for a small group of students to use. Play begins by placing the cards face down. The first player draws a card and selects from the bank the amount of money shown on the coupon. At the end of several rounds, students count together to see which player has "saved" the most money.

Restaurant

Materials

- 4 menus (made by teacher and/or students)
- real or play money
- pad
- pencil
- table
- 4 chairs

✎ Activity

Make menus by gluing pictures of foods and beverages inside file folders. Using amounts appropriate for your class, price each item on the menu. Students role-play ordering from the menu. The waiter or waitress writes (or draws) the order on a pad of paper. After "eating," each student selects the right amount of money and pays for the meal.

Chapter 16
❧ Fractions

Fractions

Before children can understand the concept of fractions, they must first think of fractions as parts of a whole which can be separated and reassembled to form the same whole (conservation of a whole). They must also understand that these fractional parts must be equal in size.

Teachers can capitalize on their students' interest in and awareness of fractions in the world around them and on their concern about sharing in fair portions. This can be done with activities that provide real-life, concrete experiences with fractional parts. The activities in this chapter include investigations of fractions as equal parts of a whole (dividing a cracker into two equal parts), as well as fractions as equal parts of a set (dividing 24 crayons into four sets of six crayons).

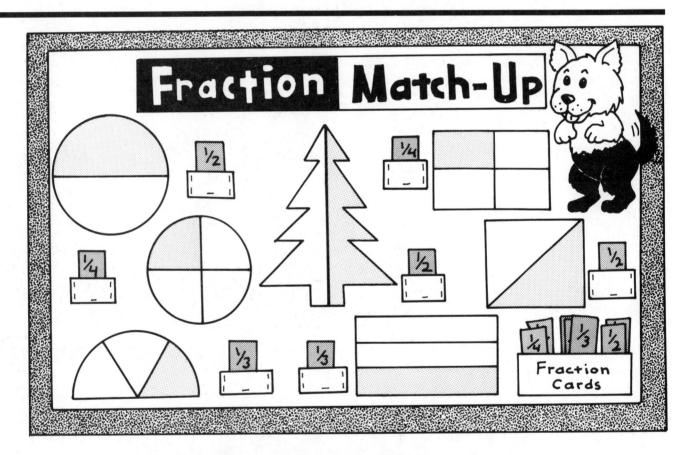

Fraction Match-Up—Bulletin Board

Cut a variety of shapes from brightly colored construction paper. Then divide each shape into halves, quarters, or thirds and shade in one fractional part. Post the shapes on the board with a shallow pocket next to each one. Write the fractions $1/2$, $1/4$, and $1/3$ on index cards. Students place the cards beside the appropriate shapes as shown above.

Skills

- Identify equal parts of a whole

- Identify equal parts of a set

- Determine how many parts make a whole

- Identify $1/2$, $1/4$, $1/3$

Learning Center

Stock the center with manipulatives that children can use to explore fractions as equal parts of a whole and equal parts of a set. Commercial materials such as pattern blocks, Cuisenaire® Rods, and plastic linking cubes are excellent.

A number of familiar classroom materials can also be effective fraction manipulatives. Supply a wide variety of paper shapes that students can fold and cut into equal parts. Set out the class math collections for students to use along with the Fraction Cards (pages 205–207).

Bring out the tub of rice used in Chapter 14, and let students fill containers $1/2$, $1/4$, or $1/3$ full. Measuring cups and measuring spoons are also good for making discoveries about parts of a whole. Provide playdough or clay so students can build their own shapes and divide them into equal parts. Don't forget to include some books that involve fractions. See page 222 for a list of titles.

The following chapter activities would also work well at a center: *Making Halves From Clay, Pattern Block Fractions, Parts of a Whole, Fruit Fractions, Rice Tub, Fractions With Math Collections, Worms in a Garden, Birthday Party Game.* (See pages 130–134.)

Activities

Are the Parts Equal?

Materials
- graham crackers, 1 per student
- paper plates, 1 per group
- paper napkins, 1 per student

✎ Activity

Divide the class into small groups. Give each child a graham cracker. (Nabisco Honey Maid® Grahams work best.) One at a time, the children break the crackers in half, show the parts to the group, and ask whether or not the parts are equal. The parts can be placed one on top of the other to help in this determination. Then the children enjoy munching the halves.

Pattern Block Fractions

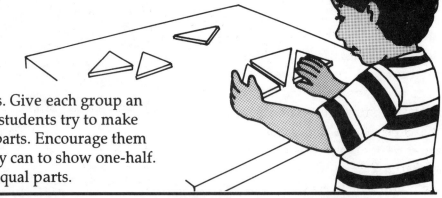

Materials
- pattern blocks

✎ Activity

Divide the class into small groups. Give each group an assortment of pattern blocks. Let students try to make different shapes from two equal parts. Encourage them to make as many examples as they can to show one-half. Then move on to three and four equal parts.

Making Halves From Clay

Materials
- clay or playdough
- plastic knives, 1 per student

✎ Activity

Give each child a ball of clay or playdough and a plastic knife. Have the children form a circle by flattening the ball into a pancake. When they are satisfied with their circle, they cut it in half. Next, have them check to see if the halves are equal by placing one on top of the other. If they are not equal, students roll a new ball and try again. Challenge them to make a square and divide it into equal halves. Have them see how many different ways a square can be divided into equal halves.

Parts of a Whole

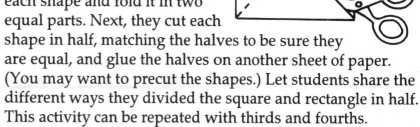

Materials
- Shape Outline Cards (page 159), 1 or 2 sets per student
- paper
- scissors
- glue

✎ Activity

Give each child a copy of page 159. Have the children cut out each shape and fold it in two equal parts. Next, they cut each shape in half, matching the halves to be sure they are equal, and glue the halves on another sheet of paper. (You may want to precut the shapes.) Let students share the different ways they divided the square and rectangle in half. This activity can be repeated with thirds and fourths.

Cookie Fractions

Materials
- Large Cookies (page 203), 1 set per student
- scissors

✎ Activity

Have each student color and cut out the cookies on page 203. Then, students divide each cookie into equal parts by cutting on the dark lines. Have them find the cookie that is cut to be shared with two people. Next, have them find the one cut for three people. Discuss why the pieces are smaller when the number of people is larger. Ask the class how many people can share the remaining large cookie. Have the children create their own story problems using these cut-up cookies.

Fruit Fractions

Materials
- Fruit Fractions (page 204), 1 set per pair
- brown paper sack, 1 per pair
- crayons or markers
- scissors

✎ Activity

Divide the class into groups of two. Have the partners color and cut out the fruit on page 204. Each fruit should also be cut into its fractional parts. Place these pieces in the sack. Players then take turns drawing a piece of fruit from the bag and laying it face up on the floor. The player who draws the piece that makes the fruit "whole" keeps the fruit, even if the other player had previously drawn matching pieces. Whoever ends up with the most whole pieces of fruit wins the game.

Rice Tub

Materials
- variety of containers marked $^1/_2$, $^1/_3$, or $^1/_4$
- rice
- tub
- drop cloth
- measuring cups

✎ Activity

Invite children to explore fractions at the rice tub by filling the various jars $^1/_2$, $^1/_3$, or $^1/_4$ full. Also provide measuring cups so students can discover how many $^1/_2$, $^1/_3$, or $^1/_4$ cups it takes to make 1 cup.

Fractions With Math Collections

Materials
- math collections, 1 per group
- yarn, 1 piece per student
- Fraction Cards (pages 205, 206, 207), 1 set per student
- transparencies of Fraction Cards for the teacher
- overhead projector

✎ Activity

Use transparencies of the Fraction Cards on the overhead projector, and model how to divide a handful of math collection objects into fair shares. As a class, count the number of objects in the fair shares to be sure they are equal. (Students will soon discover that it's not always possible to divide a given number into fair shares.)

Reproduce the Fraction Cards on heavy paper. Divide the class into groups of two or three students. Give each student a set of Fraction Cards and a piece of yarn. Ask each student to take a handful of objects from a math collection and divide the handful into two equal parts on the $^1/_2$ Fraction Card. Next, ask them to circle one-half with a piece of yarn. Repeat the activity letting students use objects from different collections.

Then have students use the $^1/_4$ Fraction Card to divide sets into four equal parts. Extend the activity by having students circle $^2/_4$ or $^3/_4$ of a whole. Proceed in the same manner with the $^1/_3$ Fraction Card.

How Much Do You Get?

Materials
- book, *The Doorbell Rang* by Pat Hutchins
- Small Cookies (page 208)
- crayons or markers
- scissors

✎ Activity

Read the book aloud for pleasure. Then have the children color and cut out the Small Cookies. Read the story a second time, and invite students to manipulate their cookies according to the action of the story. Every time more children arrive at Victoria and Sam's house, ask what each child's fair share of the cookies would be.

Afterwards, let the class make up their own story problems about cookies. One child tells a problem while the partner shows how the cookies would be divided in fair shares. For example: "Susan had six cookies. She was going to eat them all, but Alice and Lori came over so she shared them with her friends."

Parts of a Set

Materials
- plastic linking cubes, 12–20 per student

I broke my set of 8 into ¼'s.

✎ Activity

Ask students to link 12 cubes together in a "train." Have them divide the cubes into two equal sets (¹/₂) and count the number in each set. Repeat, dividing the cubes into thirds and fourths. Then ask students to make a train of 6 cubes and continue as above. The class will soon discover that this train cannot be divided into fourths.

Encourage the children to work with longer or shorter trains and divide them into fractional parts. Circulate around the room asking students to tell what fractional parts they have made. Students can also draw pictures showing how they divided each train of cubes.

Worms in a Garden

Materials

- Fraction Garden Cards (page 209), 1 set per student
- transparency of Fraction Garden Cards for the teacher
- 20 "worms" per student (made from rubber bands)
- crayons or markers
- scissors

✎ Activity

Cut small rubber bands in half for the "worms." Have students color and cut apart the Fraction Garden Cards. It's a good idea to model the activity on the overhead projector. Ask students to divide the worms equally among the four gardens and to verbalize how many $1/4$, $2/4$, or $3/4$ would be. Then instruct the class to divide the worms equally between two gardens. (Let them try dividing the worms equally among three gardens.) Do the activity another time with a different number of worms.

Birthday Party Game

Materials

- large self-sealing plastic bag, 1 per group
- 4 small birthday paper plates, 1 set per group
- 4 paper cups, 1 set per group
- 8 birthday candles, 1 set per group
- 8 straws, 1 set per group
- 8 balloons, 1 set per group
- 12 party favors or wrapped candies, 1 set per group

✎ Activity

Put all of the materials into the plastic bags. Then have the children, working in groups of four, divide the contents of the party bag into fourths. Ask students to verbalize what made up a fair share (1 plate, 2 straws, 3 favors, etc.). Repeat the activity, changing the number of children in the group and the number of items in the bag. Students will learn about fractions as they pretend to celebrate a birthday.

Chapter 17

Parent Letters

Dear Parents,

At school students use the calendar every day for a variety of activities that introduce such concepts as days of the week, months of the year, predicting and recording data, counting, and time. These concepts can easily be reinforced at home with activities like those described below:

1. When riding in the car or sitting in a waiting room, help your child say the days of the week and the months of the year in correct sequence.

2. Show your child how you use a calendar at home to remind you of future events and appointments. Point out the events that involve your child, such as soccer practice, a birthday party, or a family trip. Encourage your child to check the calendar the next time you hear the question "How many days until . . . ."

3. Show your child a variety of calendars (business calendar, purse calendar, checkbook calendar). Point out the days of the week, the months, and the year on each type of calendar.

4. Encourage your child to explain some of the things we do in class when we change the calendar, such as posting the day of the week, reciting months, making a tally for each day, graphing the weather, stringing a bead for each day, counting by ones, fives, or tens.

I hope you and your child enjoy these informal calendar activities.

Sincerely,

Dear Parents,

We have been learning about basic geometric shapes: the circle, square, rectangle, and triangle. Here are some simple activities you can do at home to help your child gain a better understanding of shapes.

1. Ask your child about our class shape walk. Use the following questions as a guide: Where did you go? What did you see? What shapes did you find? Then try a shape walk in your neighborhood.

2. At dinner, ask your child to tell you about all the shapes at the table (food, place settings, patterns on clothing, etc.).

3. Encourage your child to go on a shape search in his or her room. How many circles (squares, rectangles, triangles) did he or she find?

4. Ask your child to find five things in your house that remind him or her of shapes and draw them on the back of this paper. (Example: A door is a rectangle.)

5. Let your child use pieces of string (or toothpicks) to form different shapes.

I hope you and your child have fun with these shape activities.

Sincerely,

Dear Parents,

We have been learning about sorting and classifying things by common attributes, or characteristics. These activities help children think analytically and develop good problem-solving skills. Your child will be able to tell you about similar school experiences as you complete some of these activities together.

1. Ask your child to help with chores that involve sorting, such as folding laundry or putting away silverware.

2. Help your child organize his or her belongings. Sort objects by common attributes and place them together: stuffed animals on the bed, books grouped by size, cars all in a row, puzzles stacked on a shelf.

3. Have your child sort a variety of coins by any attribute he or she chooses (size, color, name, value). See if you can guess the attribute that was chosen. Then you sort the coins, and see if your child can guess how they were sorted.

4. Let your child sort a handful of cereal or other finger food with a variety of shapes or colors (trail mix, Chex® snack mix, mixed nuts). Ask what attributes were used. Then munch them together!

I hope you and your child have fun with these sorting activities.

Sincerely,

Patterns

Dear Parents,

We have been learning about patterns. We find patterns all around us (on wallpaper and gift wrap, in music, on furniture and clothing, in nature). Recognizing and using patterns is an important problem-solving skill for young children because pattern is an underlying theme of mathematics. Here are some pattern activities you may want to try at home:

1. Look for patterns at home. Have your child verbalize the patterns you find. (Example: "The stripes on the living room chair make a pattern: red stripe, yellow stripe, blue stripe, red stripe . . . .")

2. Have your child use common household objects to create an original pattern. (Example: fork, spoon, spoon, fork, spoon, spoon . . .)

3. Start a pattern using objects found around the house. See if your child can complete the pattern.

4. When it's time to dress for school, ask your child to look for patterns on his or her clothes.

5. Have your child draw a pattern of his or her choice on the back of this paper for another family member to finish.

Thanks for taking the time to explore this concept with your child.

Sincerely,

Dear Parents,

We have been working on counting by ones, twos, fives, and tens. There are lots of ways you can reinforce these counting skills at home. Here are a few suggestions:

1. Take a trip to the local public library, and help your child select a variety of counting books. Have fun exploring them together.

2. Give your child a set of number cards (0–10 or 0–20), and have him lay out the cards in random order. Keep track of how many minutes/seconds it takes him to put the cards in numerical order. Repeat the activity to see if he can improve his time.

3. Pop some popcorn. Take turns counting a handful of the popped kernels by ones, twos, or fives. Then munch the popcorn!

4. Play "It's Your Turn," a counting game played in class. Your child starts counting by ones, twos, fives, or tens. When she points to you, you are to continue counting until you are ready to "give it back" by pointing to her, and so on.

I know your child will appreciate working with you on some of these activities.

Sincerely,

Hands-On Math   K–1

Creative Teaching Press, Inc.

Writing Numerals

Dear Parents,

We have been working on writing the numerals 0 to 9. In addition to practice with paper and pencil, we have been painting numerals with water, walking on giant numerals, writing numerals in a salt/sand box, and making glue numerals. Ask your child about some of these activities. Here are some fun ways to reinforce this skill at home:

1. Place a cup of pudding on a large plate. Let your child "finger paint" numerals and then eat the pudding.

2. Sit with your back to your child, and have him or her use a finger to write numerals on your back. See if you can guess each one. Trade places and repeat the activity.

3. Help your child make biscuit numerals. Roll out the dough into a coil and form each coil into a different numeral. Bake and serve biscuit numerals at your next meal.

4. Let your child use foods like raisins, cereal, or nuts to form numerals on a plate.

Attached is a chart showing the way we write the numerals 0 to 9. Please use it whenever your child practices writing at home.

Sincerely,

Dear Parents,

We have been focusing on the concept of addition in our math program. Your child has had a wide variety of experiences adding, or combining, sets of objects. These concrete, manipulative experiences are essential before students can be asked to memorize addition facts.

At home, look for opportunities to incorporate addition activities into everyday routines. For example, have your child add sets of silverware while setting the table or add sets of toys at cleanup time ("3 stuffed animals plus 2 trucks equals 5 toys"). The activities listed below will also reinforce and extend classroom addition experiences. Buttons, beans, toothpicks, paper clips, or pebbles make good manipulatives for the suggested activities.

1. Encourage your child to explore a variety of ways to arrange a set of five to ten objects. For example, here are just three different ways to group five toothpicks:

2. Build three different addition problems using manipulatives. Then ask your child to write the equations.

(For example,  would be 3 + 2 = 5.)

3. Have your child use manipulatives to build the following math problems:

   2 + 4 = 6   3 + 1 = 4   5 + 0 = 5   6 + 3 = 9

Have fun exploring addition together.

Sincerely,

3+2=5

Subtraction

Dear Parents,

We have been working with a variety of manipulatives to introduce and practice the concept of subtraction. Here are some activities you and your child can do at home to help reinforce concepts covered in class.

1. Encourage your child to tell a "subtraction story" and draw a picture of the story. (Example: "Spot buried six bones in our back yard, but Lady dug two of them up. So Spot only had four bones left.")

2. Have your child use manipulatives (beans, pebbles, toothpicks, paper clips) to build the following math problems.

   $6 - 2 = 4$ $9 - 0 = 9$ $5 - 3 = 2$ $4 - 3 = 1$

3. Build three different subtraction problems using manipulatives. Have your child write the equations on the back of this paper. (Example: If you place seven beans on the table and take three away, the equation would be $7 - 3 = 4$.)

4. Integrate subtraction into your daily activities. For example, when serving a plate of sandwiches say, "Mary, I made six sandwiches. Dad ate two, how many are left?" Or when baking a cake that takes three eggs, show your child the dozen eggs. Take three out. Ask how many are left.

Sincerely,

Dear Parents,

Our current topic of study in math is the concept of place value. We have been working on grouping single objects into sets of ten and then counting aloud and verbalizing the number of objects. For example, "I counted three tens and five ones. There are 35 beans." Here are some simple activities to try at home to help reinforce your child's understanding of place value.

1. Have your child count a large handful of cereal or popcorn using groups of ten. Count another handful and compare the number of pieces in each one.

2. Have your child use small manipulatives, such as beans, toothpicks, or paper clips, to build the numbers 45, 13, and 29. Ask your child to group by tens.

3. Cut a piece of paper into 10 squares. Print the numerals 0–9, one to a square. Lay out a number of manipulatives, grouping them by tens, and have your child show the matching number cards. Take turns building the sets and using the cards.

Thank you for your help in reinforcing the concept of place value.

Sincerely,

Creative Teaching Press, Inc.

Dear Parents,

We have been working on a variety of graphing activities. We made concrete graphs using real objects, pictorial graphs, and symbolic tally graphs. We learned how to organize the information so others can easily read our graphs. Here are some graphing activities you might want to try at home.

1. Have your child make a graph of the flatware in your kitchen drawer and record the information below with pictures or tallies.

Knives	
Forks	
Spoons	

2. Have your child "read" this graph and answer the following questions. Discuss the answers.

    a. What color were the eyes of most of the kittens?

    b. What color eyes did exactly three kittens have?

    c. How many kittens were checked for eye color?

3. Help your child make a graph of the number of doors and windows in your home. Collect the data. (Count the doors and windows.) Organize the data. (Use square paper scraps for windows and rectangular scraps for doors. Glue these on a plain piece of paper in bar graph form.) Discuss the information on the graph.

                                    Sincerely,

Dear Parents,

We have been learning about estimating, or making reasonable guesses. Students have participated in a wide variety of estimation experiences. For example, they have estimated the weight of common objects, the time it takes to do a task, and the length of objects in the classroom. Here are some activities to try at home that will help reinforce the concept of estimation.

1. Fill a jar with a number of objects of the same kind (pieces of cereal, nuts, marshmallows). Ask your child to look at the container and guess how many objects are in it. Make your own guess, too. Then, together count the objects. On another day, repeat the activity with different objects.

2. Ask your child to estimate how long it will take to complete a household task, such as setting the table. Write down the estimate, then set a timer to verify. Each day let your child try to estimate the time for a different task, such as folding laundry, combing the dog, cleaning a room, or raking some leaves.

3. Give your child a small empty container, a spoon, and some uncooked rice, beans, cereal, or popcorn. Ask how many spoonfuls of rice it will take to fill the container. Then have your child count out the spoonfuls. On another day, try the activity with a different container. Was the estimate more accurate?

I hope you and your child will enjoy trying some of these estimation activities together.

Sincerely,

Dear Parents,

We have been working on developing an awareness of time by focusing on sequencing of events and duration of time. Students have also been introduced to telling time using digital and standard clocks. Here are a few activities you may want to try at home to reinforce or extend these skills.

1. Have your child guess how long it would take to complete familiar activities or tasks. For example, how long does it take to drive to the market, do the shopping, or walk to a friend's house? Then help your child time the activity to see how close the estimate was.

2. Young children show an interest in time with questions like the following: "When is it time to leave for Grandma's?" "What time will Billy be over?" When you hear a question like this, draw a simple clock showing the time and give it to your child. Encourage him or her to compare the drawing with the real clock until the two clocks match.

3. Write down a time your child is looking forward to and post it on the refrigerator. ("Your favorite TV show is at 7:00." "Sandra's birthday party starts at 2:00.") Encourage your child to come and tell you when it's time for the special event.

Leave for the movie at 1:00

4. As you go about your day, set the timer to ring on the hour or half hour. See if your child can look at a clock and tell you what time it is.

I hope you and your child enjoy doing some of these time activities.

Sincerely,

Dear Parents,

Your child has participated in a variety of measuring activities. In class we have measured the length, weight, and volume of various objects using both standard and non-standard units of measure. Since measurement is such a useful tool in our everyday lives, I hope you will be able to work together on some of the activities described below:

1. With your child, choose a non-standard unit of measure (hand, pencil, popsicle stick, envelope, etc.) and measure a variety of objects found in your home. Record your measurements on a sheet of paper.

2. Help your child use pieces of string to measure the height of each family member. Then compute the length of the string on a yardstick or a meter stick.

3. Fill a sink half full of water. Give your child a measuring cup and a variety of non-breakable containers to fill with water. Encourage your child to guess how many cups it will take to fill each container.

4. Involve your child in measuring experiences used in day-to-day activities, such as using a thermometer to measure the outside temperature or using a tape measure for sewing projects.

Let me know of any other measuring experiences you are able to share with your child. Happy measuring!

Sincerely,

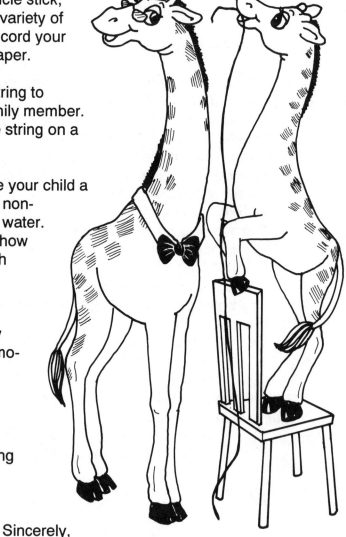

Dear Parents,

We have just finished a unit on money. We learned many ways to use coins (penny, nickel, dime, quarter) and figure values. Your child will retain this information and continue to explore money values if given many opportunities to use money in real-life situations. Here are a few activities to explore at home together:

1. Give your child a handful of coins. Let him or her identify the coins and tell you about their value.

2. Play the Penny Game. You will need at least 50 pennies. Players take turns rolling a die and taking the number of pennies indicated by the roll. After five minutes, see who has the most pennies. To make the game more difficult, use two dice and pennies, nickels, and dimes.

3. When you go to the grocery store, point out the price tags and show your child how you comparison shop for better values. At the checkout stand, point out how each item is rung up; and when you get home, look at the receipt together.

4. Help your child make small purchases at local stores or garage sales. These real-life experiences in handling money are invaluable.

I hope you will enjoy working on some of these activities together.

Sincerely,

Dear Parents,

The children have enjoyed exploring the concept of fractions at school. They have created equal parts of a whole (dividing a graham cracker into two equal pieces) as well as equal parts of a set (dividing eight cookies into two sets of four). Here are some suggestions for reinforcing the concept of fractions at home.

1. Give your child a handful of cereal or popcorn and some paper muffin cups. Ask your child to divide the cereal into two equal portions, or halves. Then encourage him or her to divide it into three (thirds) or four (fourths) equal portions by using more muffin cups.

2. Make some cookie dough (or use playdough). Invite your child to form shapes with the dough and then cut the shapes into halves, thirds, or fourths.

3. Explore fractions with water and clear, unbreakable containers. Let your child work in the sink, filling the containers one-half, one-third, or one-fourth full. Your child can also use measuring cups to discover how many $\frac{1}{2}$, $\frac{1}{3}$, or $\frac{1}{4}$ cups it takes to make 1 cup.

4. Point out the use of fractions in daily activities; for example, when filling the tub half full, measuring ingredients for a recipe, or cutting a piece of string in half.

I hope you enjoy the time you spend investigating fractions with your child.

Sincerely,

Chapter 18

Reproducibles

January

February

March

April

May

June

July

August

September

October

November

December

Bear

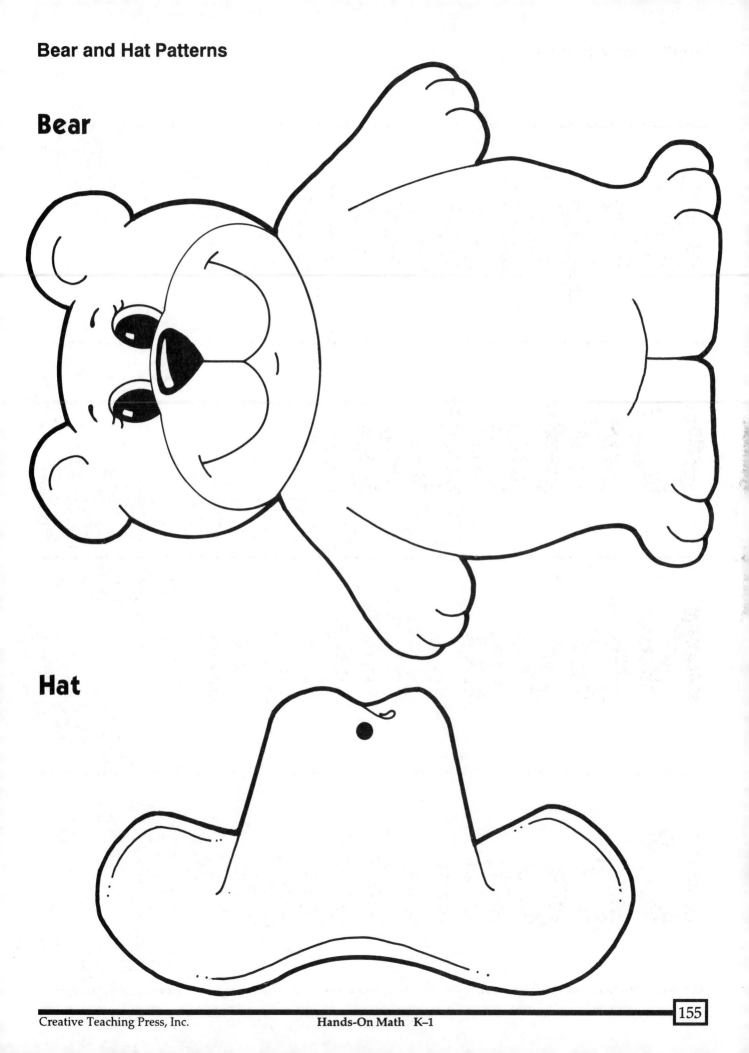

Hat

Weather Graph

_____ # Weather

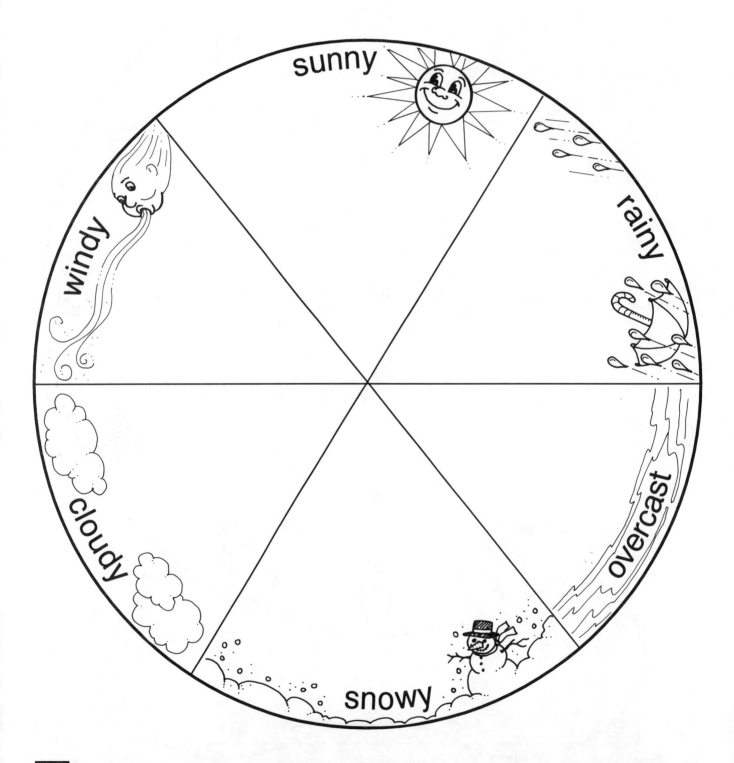

Daily Schedule Clock

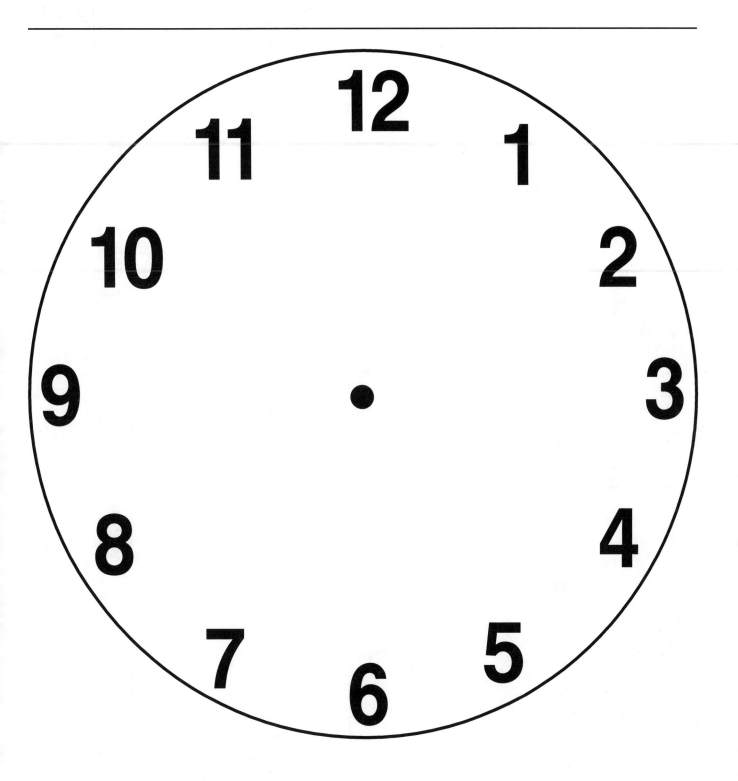

Monthly Calendar

Month _____

Year _____

Sunday	Monday	Tuesday	Wednesday	Thursday	Friday	Saturday

Creative Teaching Press, Inc.

Hands-On Math K–1

Shape Outline Cards

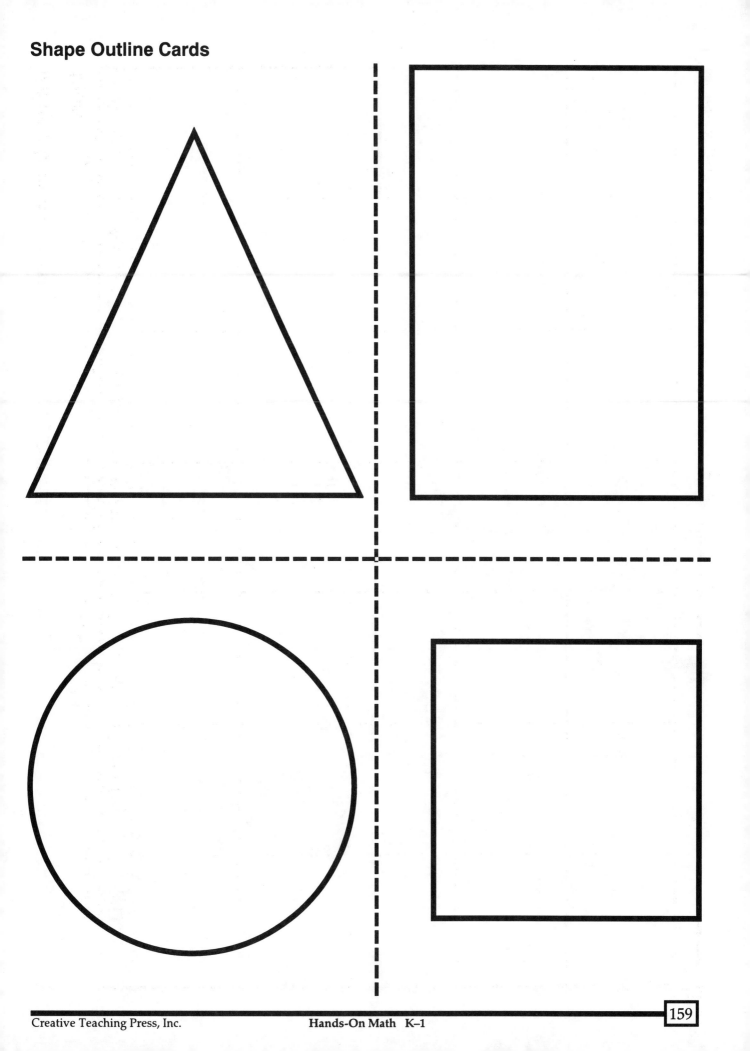

Picture Cards

Hands-On Math   K–1   Creative Teaching Press, Inc.

Creature Cards

Object Pattern Cards (Set A)

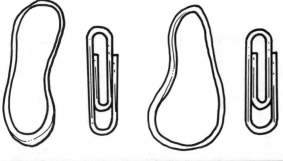

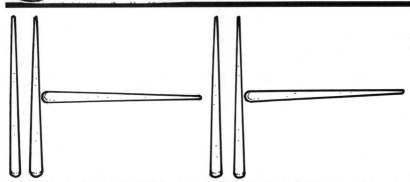

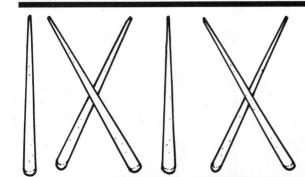

Object Pattern Cards (Set B)

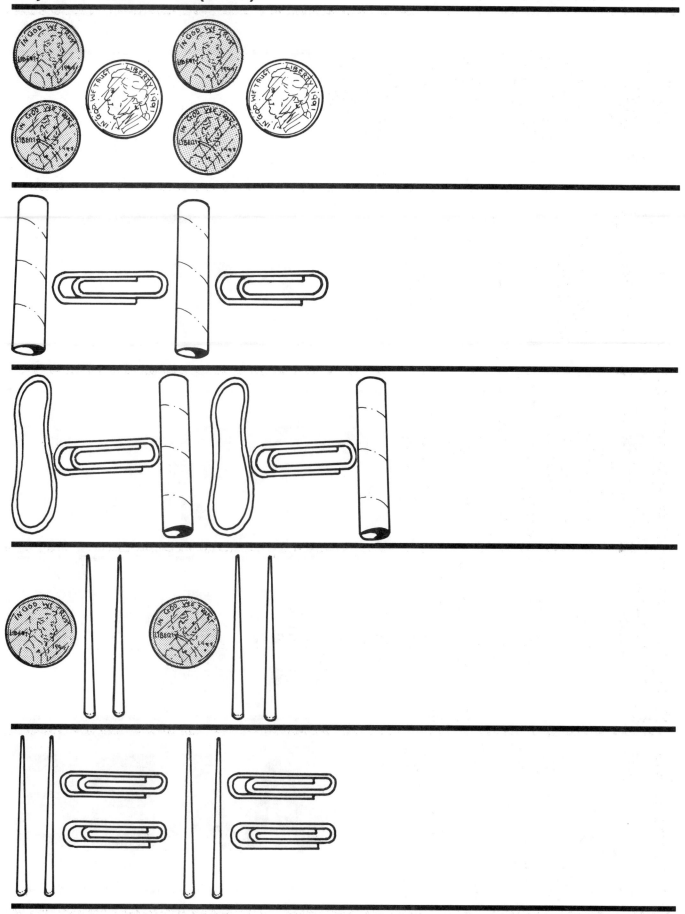

AB AB

AAB AAB

ABB ABB

ABA ABA

AABB AABB

Hands-On Math K–1 Creative Teaching Press, Inc.

Letter Pattern Cards (Set B)

ABBA ABBA

ABC ABC

ABBC ABBC

ABCB ABCB

ABCC ABCC

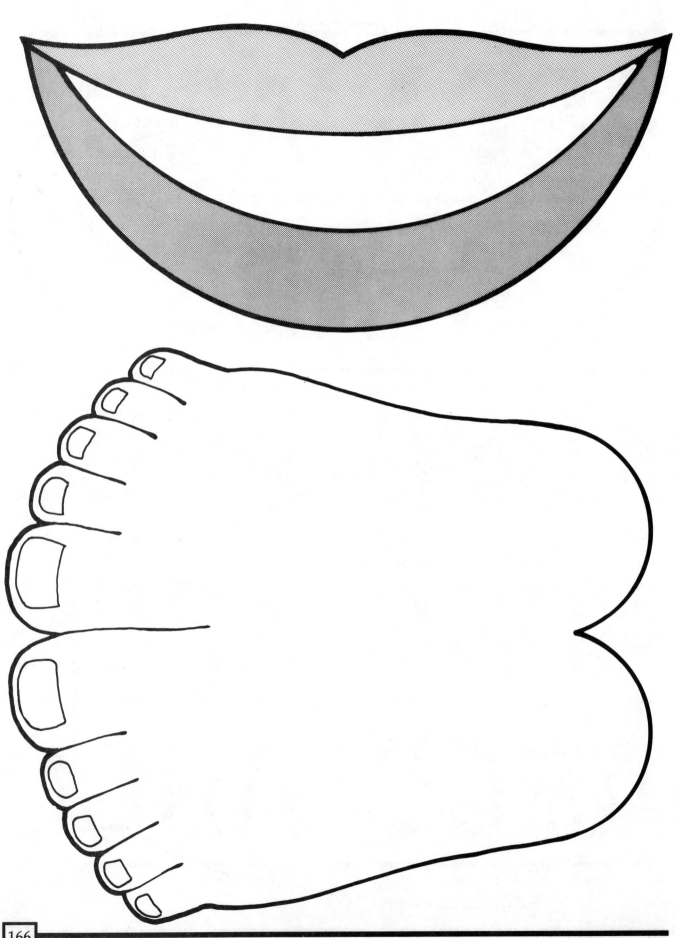

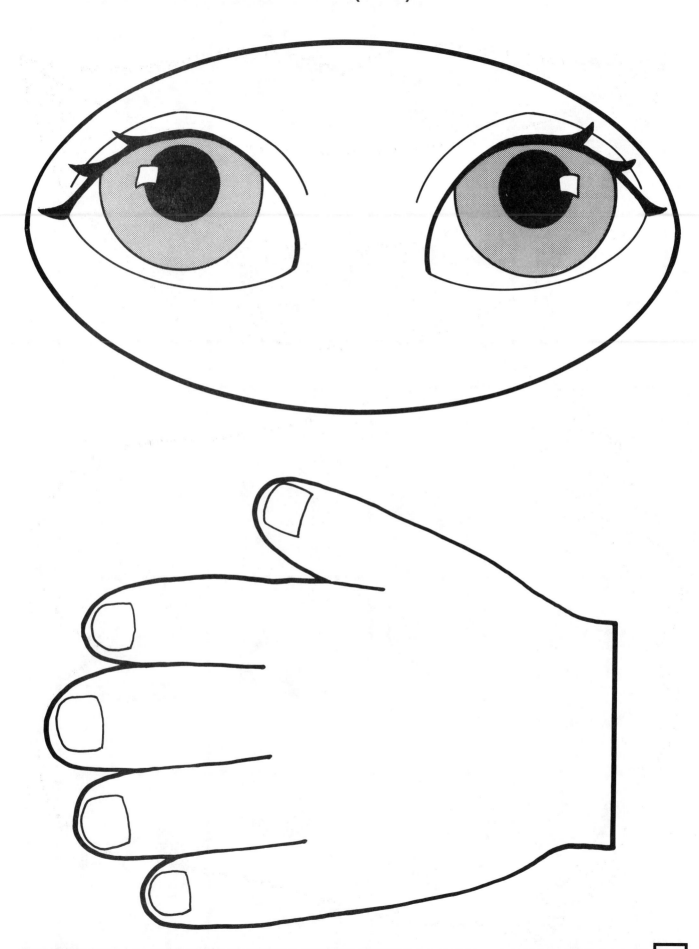

Creative Teaching Press, Inc.

1	2	3	4	5
6	7	8	9	10
11	12	13	14	15
16	17	18	19	20

Counting Recording Sheet

Name _____

What I Counted	Number I Counted

Creative Teaching Press, Inc.   Hands-On Math K–1

Numeral Patterns

1	2	3
4	5	6
7	8	9

Creative Teaching Press, Inc.

Writing Numerals

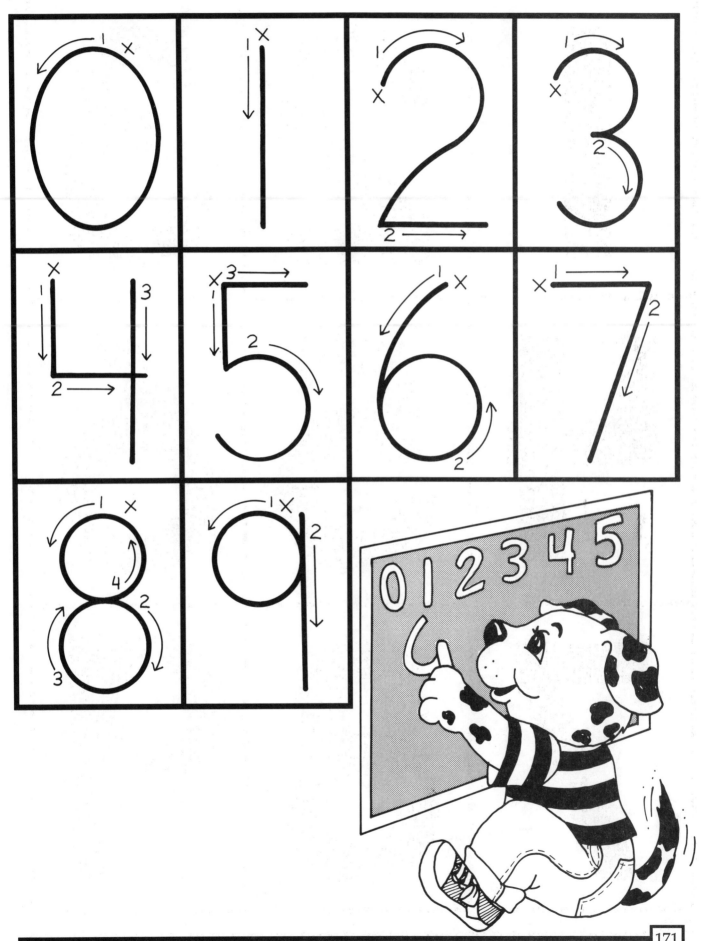

Creative Teaching Press, Inc.   Hands-On Math K–1

Creative Teaching Press, Inc.

Ant Manipulatives

Domino Dot Cards

Domino Dots Recording Sheet

Name _____

Beach Work Space Card

Use with shell collection.

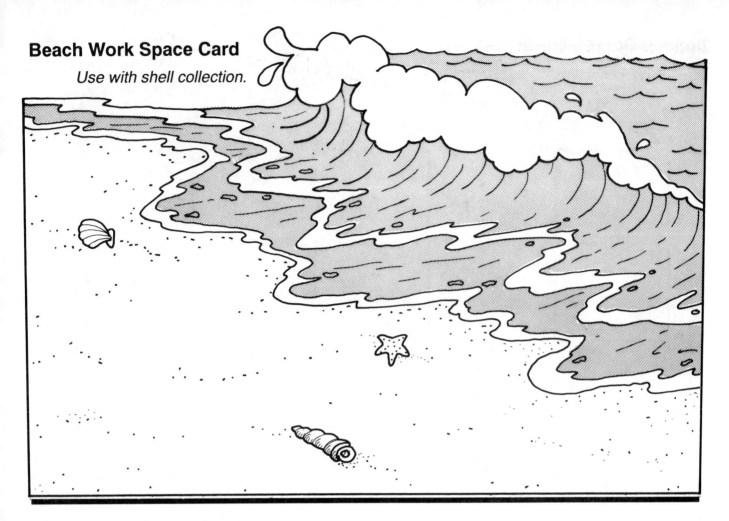

Bread Work Space Card

Use with bread tag collection.

Hands-On Math K–1

Creative Teaching Press, Inc.

Tool Box Work Space Card

Use with nuts and bolts collections.

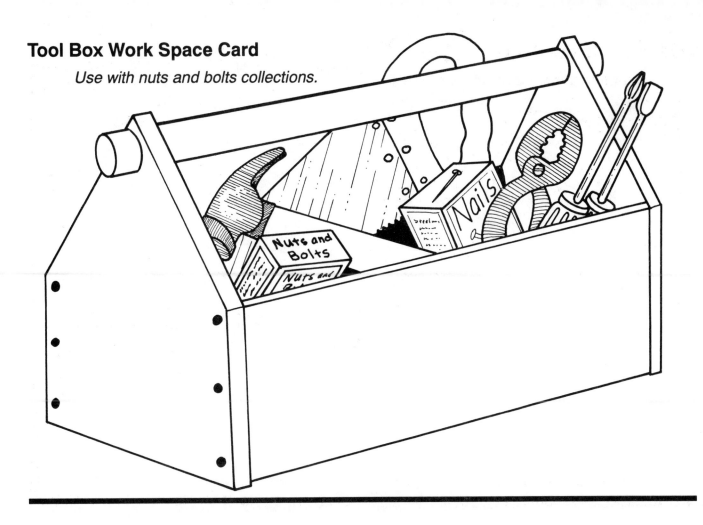

Bottles and Jars Work Space Card

Use with lid collection.

Bowl Work Space Card

Use with bean or macaroni manipulatives.

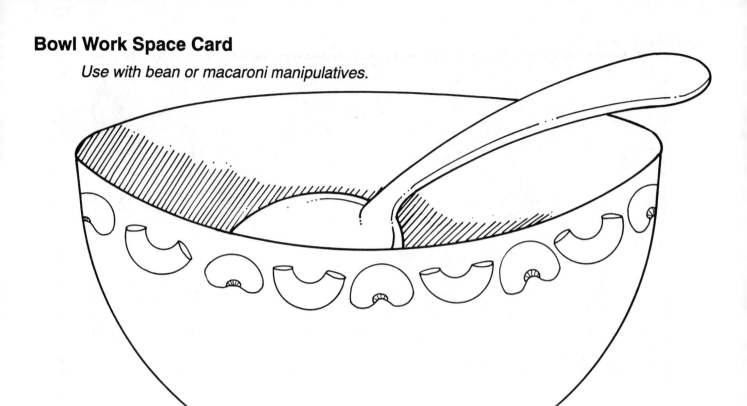

Shirt Work Space Card

Use with button collection.

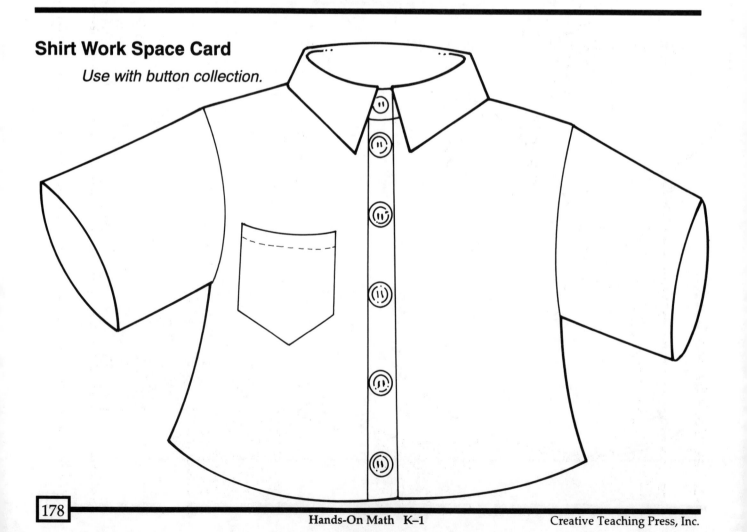

Basket Work Space Card

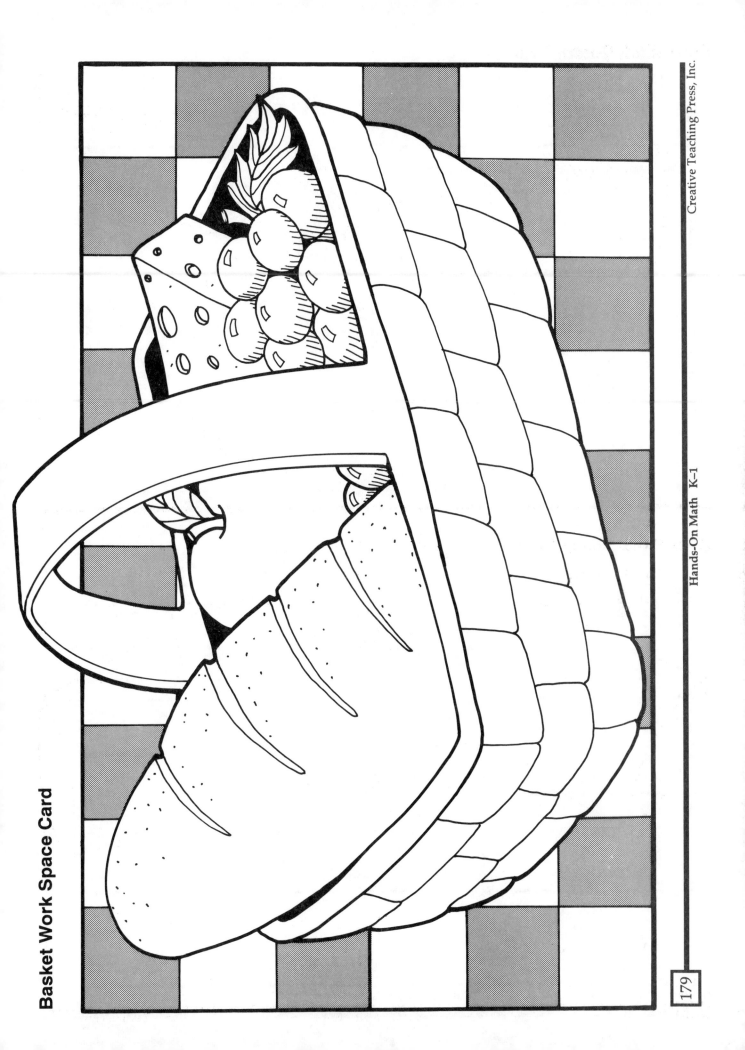

Subtraction Recording Sheet

Name _____

— _____ = _____

— _____ = _____

— _____ = _____

— _____ = _____

— _____ = _____

— _____ = _____

Hands-On Math   K–1   Creative Teaching Press, Inc.

Caterpillar and Leaf Patterns

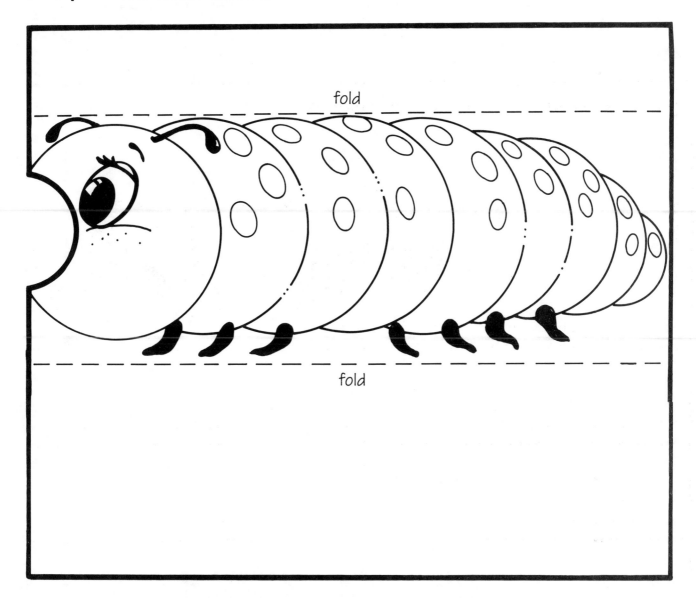

fold

fold

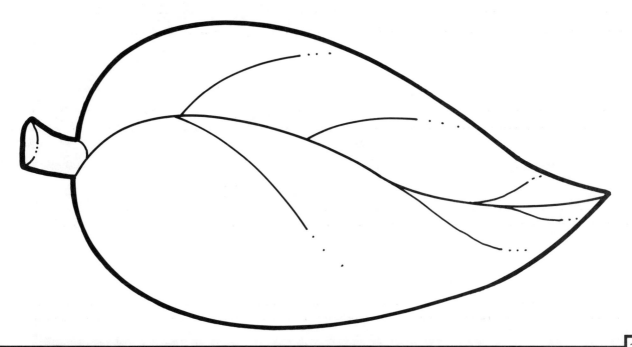

tens
10s

ones
1s

★ ★ ★ ★ ★

★ ★ ★ ★ ★

Place Value Strip Chart

Cut out the chart. Ask for help cutting the slits.

tens
10s

cut

cut

ones
1s

cut

cut

Place Value Chart Strips

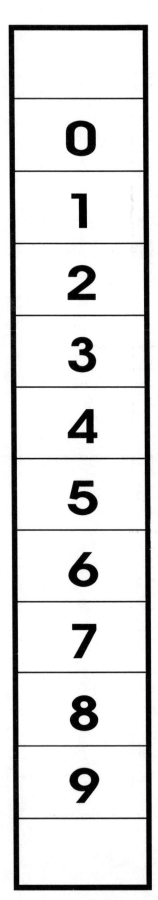

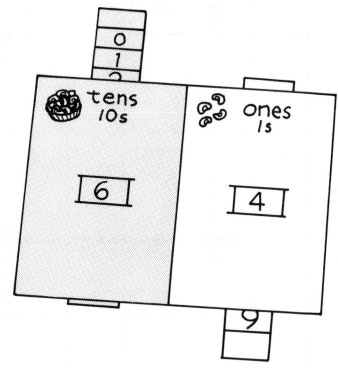

Cut out the strips. Slide them through the slits on the Place Value Chart (page 183).

Place Value Recording Sheet

Name _____

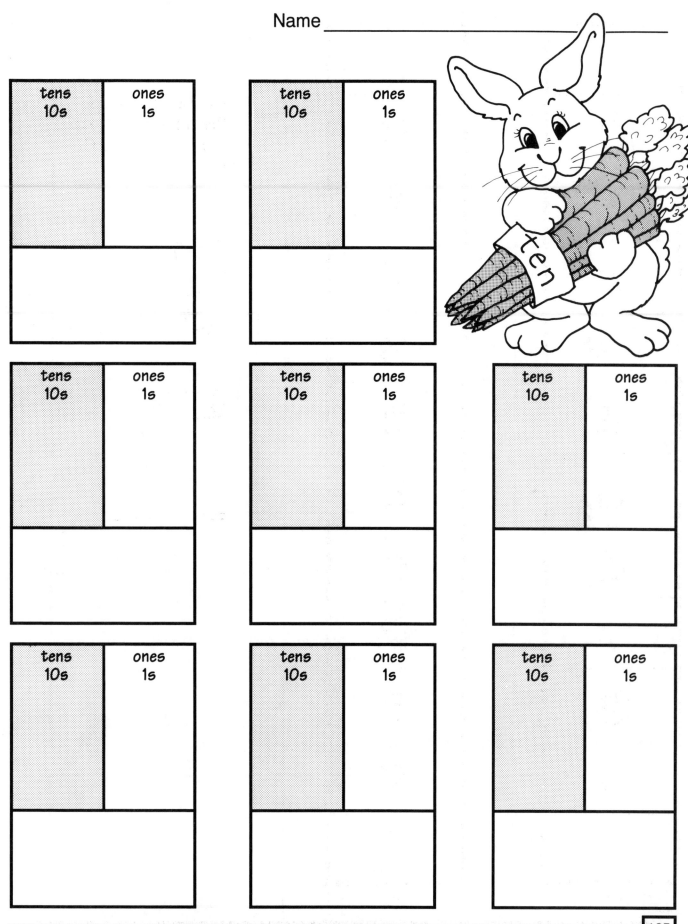

tens 10s	ones 1s

tens 10s	ones 1s

tens 10s	ones 1s

tens 10s	ones 1s

tens 10s	ones 1s

tens 10s	ones 1s

tens 10s	ones 1s

tens 10s	ones 1s

Creative Teaching Press, Inc.   Hands-On Math   K–1

Name _____

Guess and Count Cards

	Guess?	Count

Name _____

	Guess?	Count

Name _____

	Guess?	Count

Name _____

	Guess?	Count

Name _____

	Guess?	Count

Name _____

	Guess?	Count

Name _____

	Guess?	Count

Name _____

	Guess?	Count

Name _____

Creative Teaching Press, Inc.   Hands-On Math   K–1

Estimating Weight Cards

Hands-On Math K–1

Creative Teaching Press, Inc.

Estimating Time Cards

Tie your shoe.

Write your name.

Sing "Happy Birthday."

Touch your toes 15 times.

Count aloud to 30.

...26, 27, 28, 29, 30.

Walk around the room.

Read a favorite book aloud.

Do 10 sit-ups.

Cut a square.

Write from 1–10.

Sing the alphabet.

A B C D E F...

Wash a table.

Prediction Sheet

Name _____

	Guess?	Guess?	
	Time	Time	
	Guess?	Guess?	
	Time	Time	
	Guess?	Guess?	
	Time	Time	
	Guess?	Guess?	
	Time	Time	
	Guess?	Guess?	
	Time	Time	

Hands-On Math K–1   Creative Teaching Press, Inc.

Standard Clock

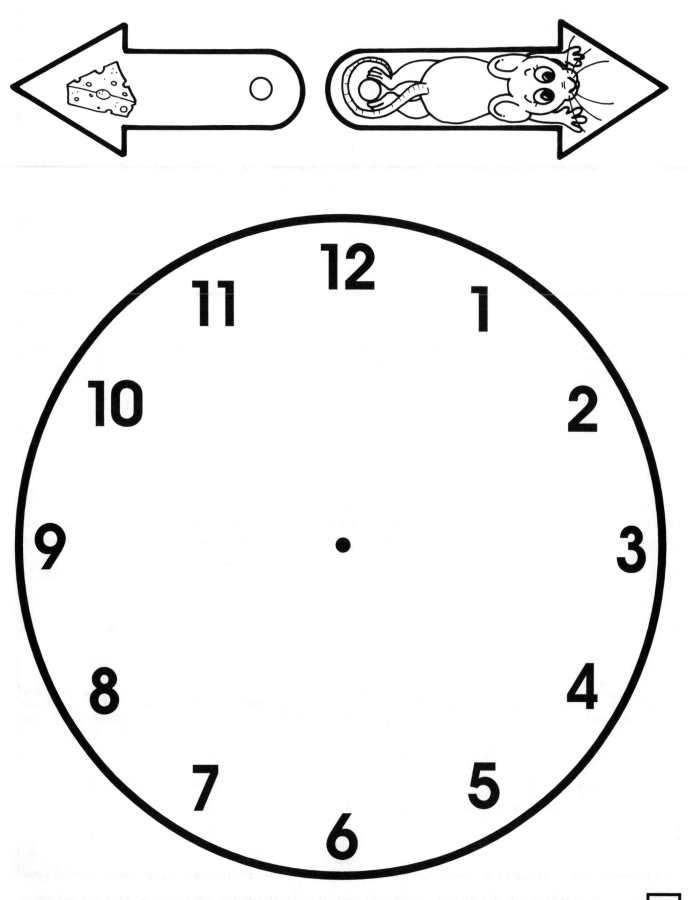

Digital Clock

1. Color and cut out the clock. Cut the two slits.
2. Cut out and glue the hour (and half-hour) strips together.
3. Slide a strip through the slits on the clock.

| 1:00 | 2:00 | 3:00 | 4:00 | 5:00 | 6:00 | 7:00 |

| glue | 8:00 | 9:00 | 10:00 | 11:00 | 12:00 |

| 1:30 | 2:30 | 3:30 | 4:30 | 5:30 | 6:30 | 7:30 |

| glue | 8:30 | 9:30 | 10:30 | 11:30 | 12:30 |

Standard Clock Faces

Digital Clock Faces

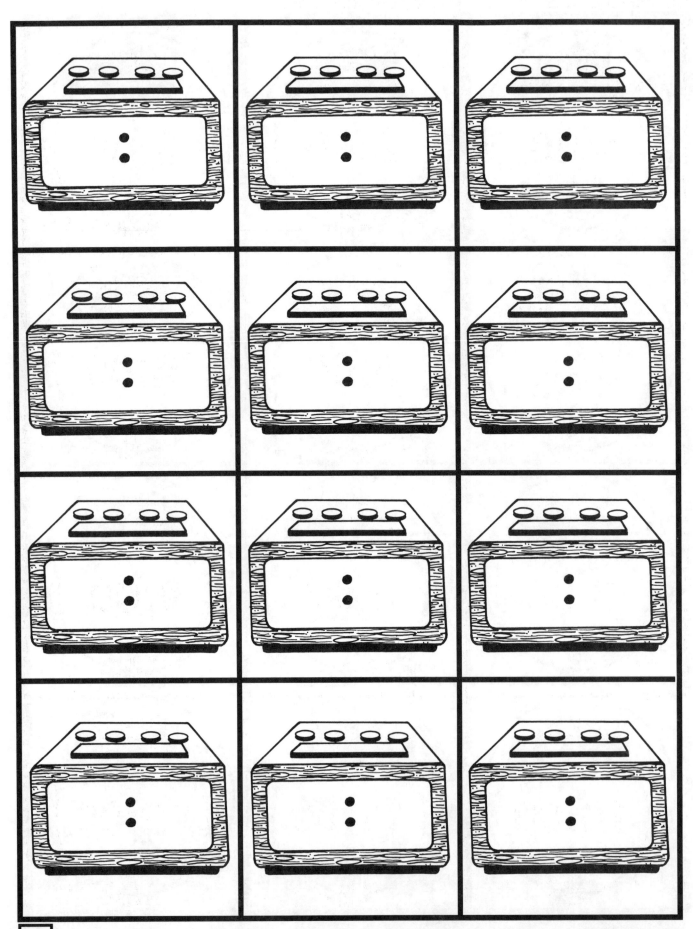

Hands-On Math K–1

Creative Teaching Press, Inc.

Ladybug Cards

Cut the cards apart for the Grouchy Ladybug Game.

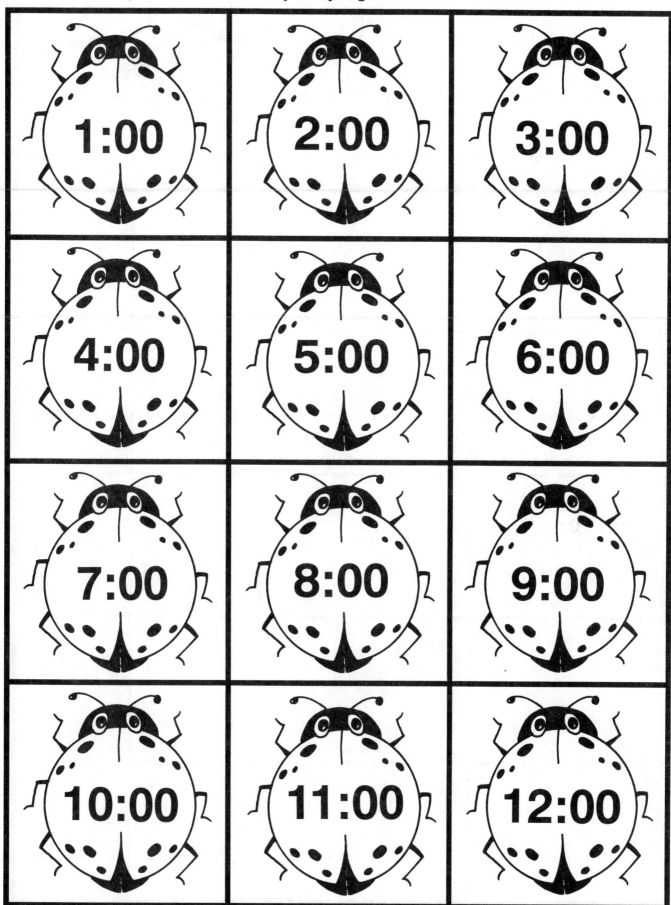

Measurement Recording Sheet

Name _____

What I Measured	I Measured With	My Guess	Measurement

Hands-On Math   K–1   Creative Teaching Press, Inc.

Rulers

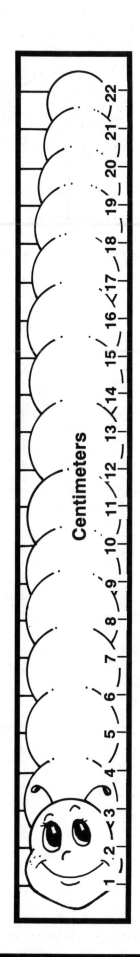

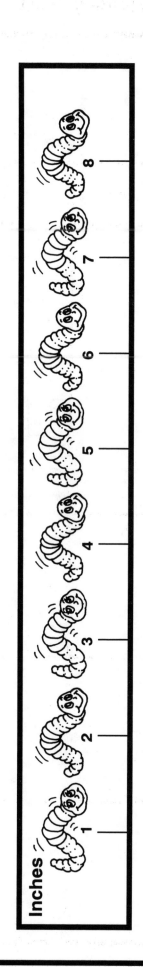

Clothing Game

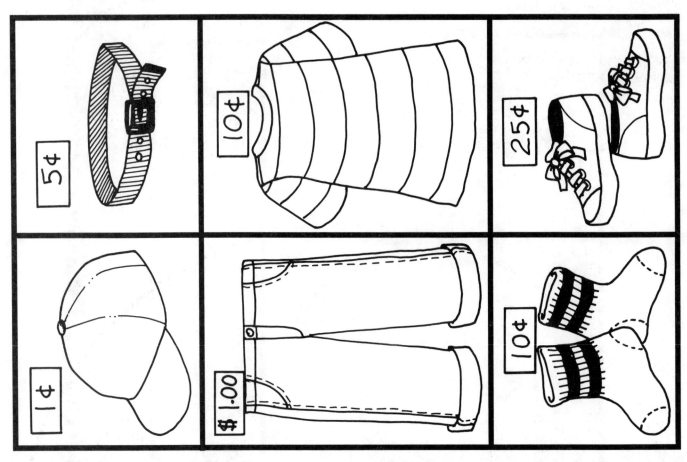

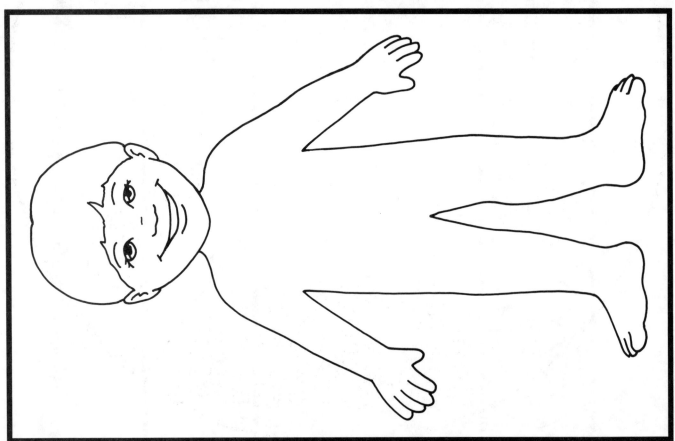

Hands-On Math K–1

Creative Teaching Press, Inc.

Money Spinner

Reproduce on tagboard.

Insert a paper fastener in the center.

Loop a large paper clip over the paper
fastener for a spinner.

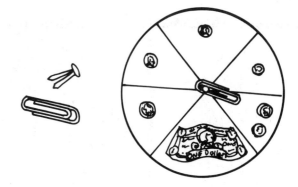

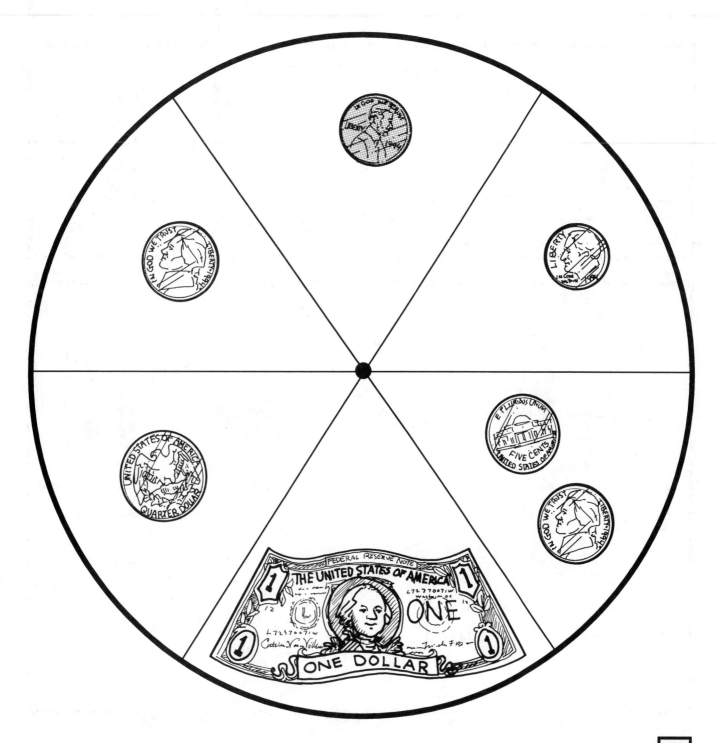

Things to Buy (Set A)

Hands-On Math   K–1   Creative Teaching Press, Inc.

Things to Buy (Set B)

Coins

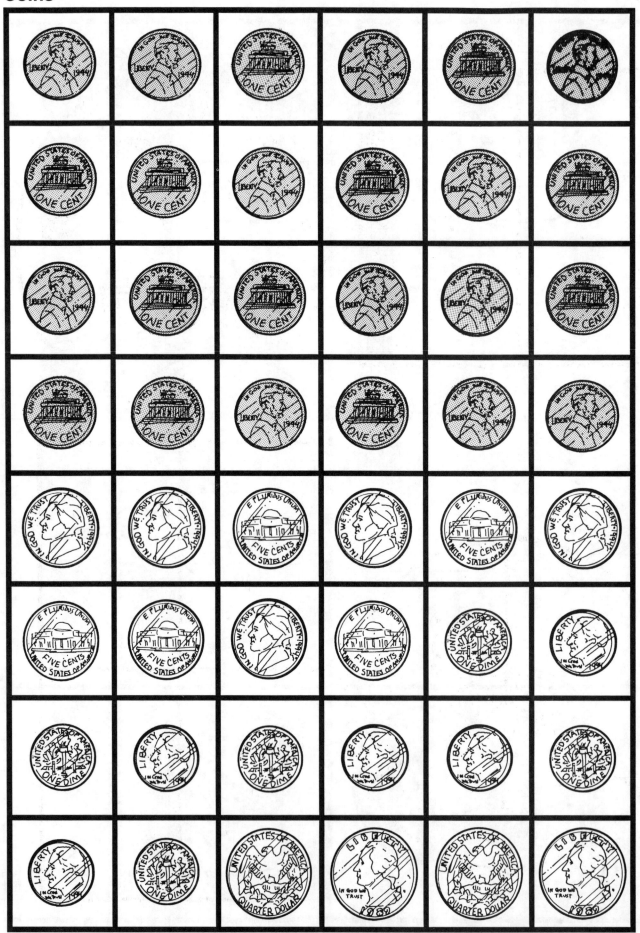

Hands-On Math K–1

Large Cookies

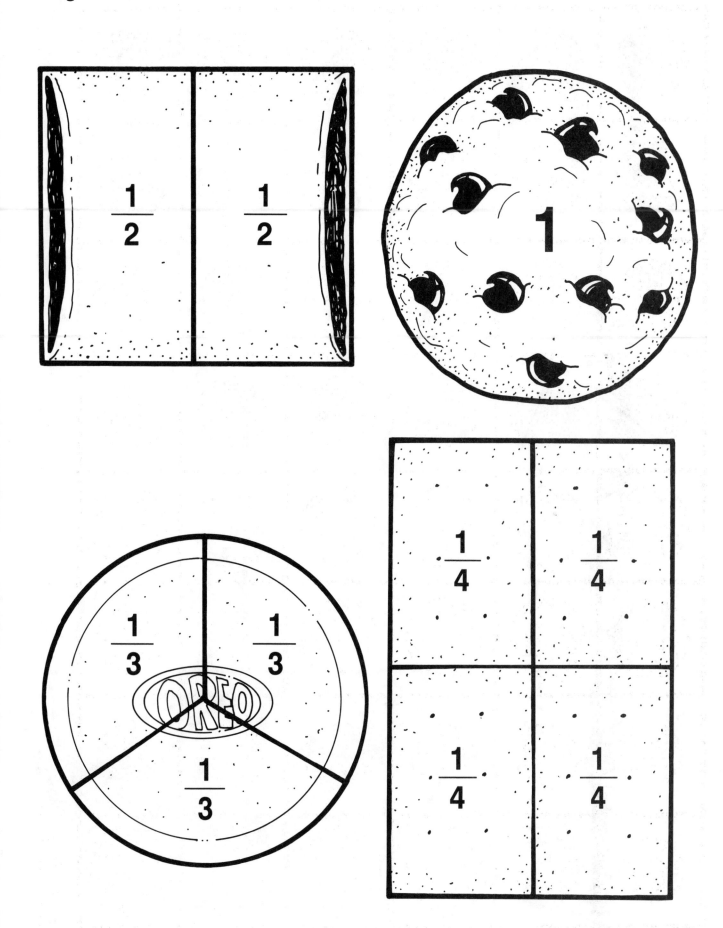

Fruit Fractions

Hands-On Math K–1

Creative Teaching Press, Inc.

Fraction Card (1/2)

$$\frac{1}{2}$$

$$\frac{1}{2}$$

$$\frac{1}{4}$$

$$\frac{1}{4}$$

$$\frac{1}{4}$$

$$\frac{1}{4}$$

Fraction Card (1/3)

$\dfrac{1}{3}$

$\dfrac{1}{3}$

$\dfrac{1}{3}$

Small Cookies

Hands-On Math   K–1

Creative Teaching Press, Inc.

Fraction Garden Cards

Color and cut out the 4 gardens.

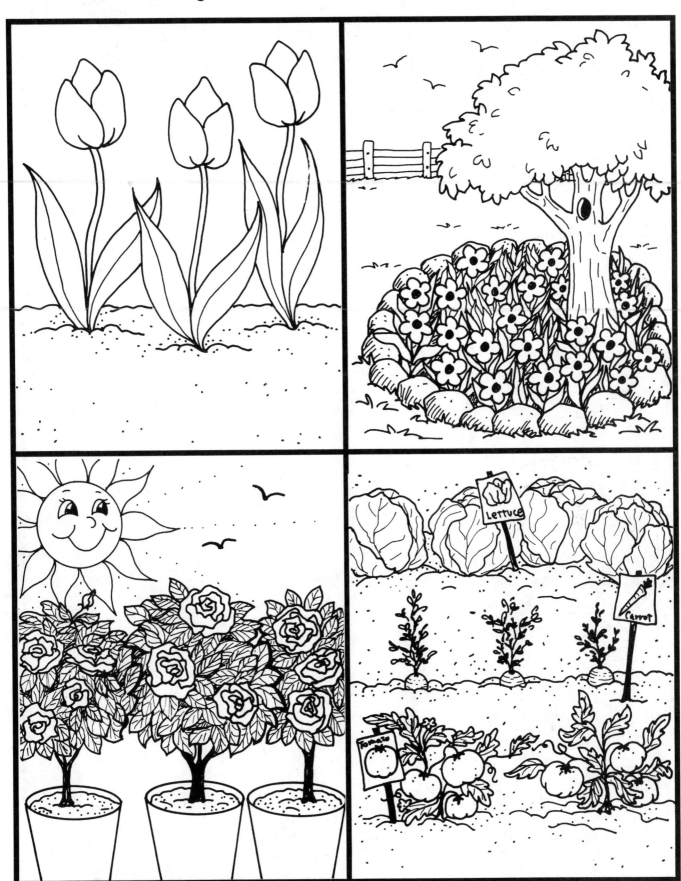

Hands-On Math K–1

Notes

Hands-On Math   K–1

Creative Teaching Press, Inc.

Chapter 19

Related Literature

Related Literature

Use selections from the following lists to integrate math and literature in a variety of ways. A favorite book can be used to introduce a math concept or a specific skill. For example, *Ten, Nine, Eight* by Molly Bang makes an excellent introduction to the skill of counting backwards. A story can extend students' mathematical thinking. The class, for instance, can create story problems for the events in *The Doorbell Rang* by Pat Hutchins. Or a book can be used at the conclusion of a unit to assist in the review process. Eric Carle's book *The Grouchy Ladybug*, for example, can help reinforce telling time skills.

Calendar

Allington, Richard. *Autumn*. Raintree, 1981.
———. *Spring*. Raintree, 1981.
———. *Summer*. Raintree, 1981.
———. *Winter*. Raintree, 1981.
Barklem, Jill. *Autumn Story*. Putnam, 1980.
———. *Spring Story*. Putnam, 1980.
———. *Summer Story*. Putnam, 1980.
———. *Winter Story*. Putnam, 1980.
Carle, Eric. *Today Is Monday*. Philomel, 1993.
———. *The Very Hungry Caterpillar*. Putnam, 1981.
Clifton, Lucille. *Some of the Days of Everett Anderson*. Holt, 1983.
dePaola, Tomie. *Four Stories for Four Seasons*. Prentice-Hall, 1977.
Hawkins, Colin. *Mr. Wolf's Week*. Collins Publishing, 1985.
Hutchins, Pat. *Changes, Changes*. Macmillan, 1987.
Keenan, George. *The Preposterous Week*. Dial, 1971.
Maestro, Betsy. *Through the Year With Harriet*. Crown, 1985.
Marshak, Samuel. *The Month Brothers*. Morrow, 1983.
Marshall, Edward. *Fox All Week*. Dial, 1984.
Provensen, Alice. *The Year at Maple Hill Farm*. Atheneum, 1978.
Russo, Marisabina. *Only Six More Days*. Greenwillow, 1988.
Sendak, Maurice. *Chicken Soup With Rice*. Harper & Row, 1962.
Tafuri, Nancy. *All Year Long*. Greenwillow, 1983.
Ward, Cindy. *Cookie's Week*. Putnam, 1988.

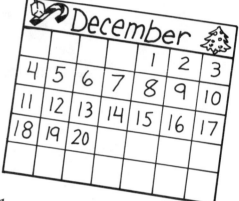

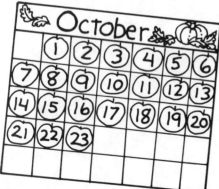

Geometric Shapes

Barrett, Peter and Susan. *The Circle Sarah Drew*. Scroll Press, Inc., 1973.

———. *The Square Ben Drew*. Scroll Press, Inc., 1973.

Brown, Marcia. *Listen to a Shape*. Watts, 1979.

Eberts, Marjorie and Margaret Gisler. *Pancakes, Crackers, and Pizza: A Book of Shapes*. Childrens Press, 1984.

Ehlert, Lois. *Color Farm*. HarperCollins, 1990.

———. *Color Zoo*. HarperCollins, 1990.

Falwell, Cathryn. *Shape Space*. Clarion, 1992.

Feldman, Judy. *Shapes in Nature*. Childrens Press, 1991.

Fisher, Leonard Everett. *Look Around! A Book About Shapes*. Viking, 1987.

Gillham, Bill. *Let's Look for Shapes*. Putnam, 1984.

Grifalconi, Ann. *The Village of Round and Square Houses*. Little, Brown and Co., 1986.

Hoban, Tana. *Circles, Triangles, and Squares*. Macmillan, 1974.

———. *Round and Round and Round*. Greenwillow, 1983.

———. *Shapes and Things*. Macmillan, 1970.

———. *Shapes, Shapes, Shapes*. Greenwillow, 1985.

Hughes, Shirley. *All Shapes and Sizes*. Lothrop, Lee & Shepard, 1986.

Hutchins, Pat. *Changes, Changes*. Macmillan, 1987.

Knightley, Rosalinda. *Shapes*. Little, Brown and Co., 1986.

Reiss, John J. *Shapes*. Viking Press, 1991.

Srivastava, Jane. *Spaces, Shapes, and Sizes*. Crowell Junior Books, 1980.

Wildsmith, Brian. *Animal Shapes*. Oxford, 1980.

Sorting and Classifying

Ahlberg, Janet and Allan. *The Baby's Catalog.* Little, Brown and Co., 1983

Anno, Mitsumasa. *Anno's Flea Market.* Putnam, 1984.

Brenner, Barbara. *Mr. Small and Mr. Tall.* Addison-Wesley, 1966.

Brett, Jan. *Goldilocks and the Three Bears.* Dodd. 1987.

Eastman, Philip C. *Big Dog, Little Dog.* Random House, 1973.

Fey, James. *Long, Short, High, Low, Thin, Wide.* T.Y. Crowell Junior Books, 1961.

Galdone, Paul. *The Three Billy Goats Gruff.* Clarion, 1973.

Hawkinson, John and Lucy. *The Little Boy Who Lives Up High.* Whitman Books, 1967.

Hoban, Russell. *Ten What?* Scribner's, 1975.

Hoban, Tana. *Big Ones, Little Ones.* Greenwillow, 1976.

———. *Is It Red? Is It Yellow? Is It Blue?* Greenwillow, 1978.

Morris, Ann. *Hats, Hats, Hats.* Lothrop, Lee & Shepard, 1989.

Pienkowski, Jan. *Sizes.* Puffin Books, 1983.

Spier, Peter. *Fast-Slow, High-Low: A Book of Opposites.* Doubleday, 1972.

———. *Gobble, Growl, Grunt.* Doubleday, 1971.

———. *People.* Doubleday, 1980.

Wells, Tony. *Allsorts.* Macmillan, 1988.

Winthrop, Elizabeth. *Shoes.* Harper & Row, 1986.

Zemach, Margot. *The Three Little Pigs.* Farrar, Straus and Giroux, 1988.

Patterns

Books with repeated language patterns:

Alderson, SueAnn. *Hurry Up, Bonnie.* Tree Frog Press, 1977.

Bayer, Jane. *A My Name Is Alice.* Dial, 1984.

Brown, Margaret Wise. *Goodnight Moon.* Harper & Row, 1947.

Carle, Eric. *Have You Seen My Cat?* Picture Book Studio, 1991.

Emberley, Barbara. *Drummer Hoff.* Treehouse Productions, 1967.

Ginsburg, Mirra. *The Chick and the Duckling.* Macmillan, 1972.

Hutchins, Pat. *Good-Night, Owl!* Macmillan, 1972.

———. *1 Hunter.* Greenwillow, 1982.

———. *Rosie's Walk.* Macmillan, 1968.

Kalan, Robert. *Jump, Frog, Jump!* Greenwillow, 1981.

Mayer, Mercer. *Just for You.* Golden Press, 1975.

Peek, Merle. *Mary Wore Her Red Dress.* Clarion, 1985

Shaw, Charles. *It Looked Like Spilt Milk.* Harper & Row, 1947.

Tafuri, Nancy. *Have You Seen My Duckling?* Greenwillow, 1984.

Wildsmith, Brian. *Cat on the Mat.* Oxford, 1987.

Looking for patterns in the environment:

Eberts, Marjorie and Margaret Gesler. *Pancakes, Crackers, and Pizza.* Childrens Press, 1984.

Feldman, Judy. *Shapes in Nature.* Childrens Press, 1991.

Fisher, Leonard Everett. *Look Around.* Viking Press,

Hoban, Tana. *Circles, Triangles, and Squares.* Macmillan, 1974.

———. *I Read Signs.* Greenwillow, 1983.

———. *Look Again!* Macmillan, 1971.

———. *Shapes and Things.* Macmillan, 1970.

———. *Shapes, Shapes, Shapes.* Greenwillow, 1986.

———. *Spirals, Curves, Fanshapes and Lines.* Greenwillow, 1992.

McMillan, Bruce. *Fire Engine Shapes.* Lothrop, Lee & Shepard, 1988

Numbers and Counting

Anderson, SaraLee. *Numbers.* Dutton, 1988.

Anno, Mitsumasa. *Anno's Counting Book.* HarperCollins, 1977.

Bennett, David. *One Cow Moo Moo!* Henry Holt, 1990.

Bradman, Tony. *Not Like That, Like This.* Oxford, 1989.

Brown, Marc. *One, Two, Three: An Animal Counting Book,* Little, Brown and Co., 1976.

Bruna, Dick. *I Know More About Numbers.* Methuen, 1981.

Burningham, John. *The Shopping Basket.* Harper Junior Books, 1980.

Carle, Eric. *Rooster's Off to See the World.* Picture Book Studio, 1987.

———. *The Very Hungry Caterpillar.* Putnam, 1989.

Clement, Rod. *Counting on Frank.* Gareth Stevens, 1991.

Ehlert, Lois. *Fish Eyes: A Book You Can Count On.* Harcourt Brace Jovanovich, 1991.

Ernst, Lisa. *Up to Ten and Down Again.* Lothrop, Lee & Shepard, 1986.

Falwell, Cathryn. *Feast for 10.* Clarion Books, 1993.

Fleming, Denise. *Count!* Henry Holt, 1992.

Giganti, Paul. *How Many Snails?* Greenwillow, 1988.

———. *Each Orange Had Eight Slices.* Greenwillow, 1992.

Gretz, Susanna. *Teddy Bears Go Shopping.* Macmillan, 1982.

Hinchcliffe, Jo. *The Hilton Hen House.* Ashton Scholastic, 1987.

Hoban, Tana. *Count and See.* Macmillan, 1972.

Hutchins, Pat. *1 Hunter.* Greenwillow, 1982.

Kuskin, Karla. *The Dallas Titans Get Ready for Bed.* Harper & Row, 1986.

Lobel, Arnold. "A Lost Button" in *Frog and Toad Are Friends,* Harper & Row, 1983.

McMillan, Bruce. *Counting Wildflowers.* Lothrop, Lee & Shepard, 1986.

Raffi, *Five Little Ducks.* Crown, 1990.

Serfozo, Mary. *Who Wants One?* McElderry, 1990.

Seuss, Dr. *Ten Apples Up on Top.* Random House, 1988.

Sheppard, Jeff. *The Right Number of Elephants.* Harper & Row, 1990.

Walsh, Ellen Stoll. *Mouse Count.* Harcourt Brace Jovanovich, 1991.

Wylie, Joanne and David. *How Many Monsters?* Childrens Press, 1985.

Writing Numerals

Bang, Molly. *Ten, Nine, Eight.* Greenwillow, 1983.

Carle, Eric. *1, 2, 3, at the Zoo.* Philomel, 1968.

Ehlert, Lois. *Fish Eyes.* Harcourt Brace Jovanovich, 1990.

Grossman, Virginia. *Ten Little Rabbits.* Chronicle Books, 1991.

Hoban, Tana. *1, 2, 3.* Greenwillow, 1985.

Hulme, Joy. *Sea Squares.* Hyperion, 1991.

Hutchins, Patricia. *1 Hunter.* Greenwillow, 1982.

Inkpen, Mick. *One Bear at Bedtime.* Little, Brown and Co., 1987.

McMillan, Bruce. *Counting Wildflowers.* Lothrop, Lee & Shepard, 1986.

Mitsumasa, Anno. *Anno's Counting Book.* T.Y. Crowell, 1977.

Morozumi, Atsuko. *One Gorilla.* Farrar, Straus & Giroux, 1990.

Pallotta, Jerry. *The Icky Bug Counting Book.* Charlesbridge, 1991.

Reiss, John. *Numbers.* Bradbury Press. 1971.

Thornhill, Jan. *The Wildlife 1, 2, 3.* Simon & Schuster, 1989.

Ungerer, Tomi. *Crictor.* Harper & Row, 1983.

Addition

Bang, Molly. *Ten, Nine, Eight.* Greenwillow, 1983.

Bogart, J. *10 for Dinner.* Scholastic, 1989.

Burningham, John. *Pigs Plus: Learning Addition.* Viking, 1983.

Crews, Donald. *Ten Black Dots.* Greenwillow, 1986.

Farber, Norma. *Up the Down Elevator.* Addison-Wesley, 1979.

Gisler, Davie. *Addition Annie.* Childrens Press, 1991.

Grossman, Virginia. *Ten Little Rabbits.* Chronicle, 1991.

Irons, D. *Even Steven.* Rigby, 1987.

McMillan, Bruce. *Here a Chick, There a Chick.* Lothrop, Lee & Shepard, 1988.

Morozumi, Atsuko. *One Gorilla.* Farrar, Straus & Giroux, 1990.

Nelson, JoAnne. *One and One Make Two.* Modern Curriculum Press, 1990.

Samton, Sheila. *Moon to Sun: An Adding Book.* Boyds Mills Press, 1991.

———. *On the River: An Adding Book.* Boyds Mills Press, 1991.

Schwartz, David. *How Much Is a Million?* Scholastic, 1985.

Subtraction

Anno, Mitsumasu. *Anno's Counting House.* Philomel, 1982.

Bate, Lucy. *Little Rabbit's Loose Tooth.* Crown, 1975.

Burningham, John. *Ride Off: Learning Subtraction.* Viking, 1983.

————. *The Shopping Basket.* T.Y. Crowell, 1980.

Carle, Eric. *Rooster's Off to See the World.* Picture Book Studio, 1972.

Christelow, Eileen. *Five Little Monkeys Jumping on the Bed.* Clarion, 1989.

Gackenbach, Dick. *A Bag Full of Pups.* Clarion, 1991.

Giganti, Paul. *How Many Snails?* Greenwillow, 1988.

Hawkins, Colin. *Take Away Monsters.* Putnam, 1984.

Hoban, Russell, *A Birthday for Frances.* Harper & Row, 1976.

Irons, D. *The Mean Machine.* Rigby, 1987.

Maestro, Guilio. *One More and One Less.* Crown, 1974.

Mahy, Margaret. *17 Kings and 42 Elephants.* Penguin Press, 1990.

————. *The Boy Who Was Followed Home.* Penguin Press, 1986.

Mathews, Louise. *The Great Take Away.* Dodd, 1980.

Nordquist, Sven. *Willie in the Big World.* Morrow, 1986.

Raffi. *Five Little Ducks.* Crown, 1989.

Russo, M. *Only Six More Days.* Greenwillow, 1988.

Tafuri, Nancy. *Have You Seen My Duckling?* Greenwillow, 1984.

Place Value

Asch, Frank. *Popcorn.* Parents', 1979.

Charlip, Remy. *Thirteen.* Parents', 1975.

du Bois, William Pene. *The Twenty-one Balloons.* Puffin Books, 1989.

Gantz, David. *Captain Swifty Counts to 50.* Doubleday, 1982.

Gardner, Beau. *Can You Imagine . . . ?* Dodd, Mead, 1987.

Gillen, Patricia. *My Signing Book of Numbers.* Gallaudet University Press, 1987.

Howard, Katherine. *I Can Count to 100 . . . Can You?* Random House, 1979.

Meddaugh, Susan. *Too Many Monsters.* Houghton Mifflin, 1982.

Raskin, Ellen. *Twenty-two, Twenty-three.* Atheneum, 1976.

Schwartz, David. *How Much Is a Million?* Scholastic, 1985.

Seuss, Dr. *The 500 Hats of Bartholomew Cubbins.* Vanguard Press, 1938.

Sharmat, Marjorie. *The 329th Friend.* Four Winds, 1979.

Shepperson, Bob. *The Sandman.* Farrar, Straus & Giroux, 1989.

Sitomer, Mindel & Harry. *Zero Is Not Nothing.* Crowell Jr. Books, 1978.

Sloat, Teri. *From One to One Hundred.* Dutton, 1991.

Zaslavsky, Claudia. *Zero! Is It Something? Is It Nothing!* Franklin Watts, 1989.

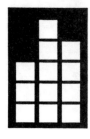

Graphing

Books for concrete and pictorial graphing of story characters:

Allen, Pamela. *Mr. Archimedes' Bath*. HarperCollins, 1985.
Carle, Eric. *The Very Busy Spider*. Putnam, 1989.
———. *The Very Hungry Caterpillar*. Putnam, 1989.
Comber, Barbara. *Dad's Diet*. Ashton Scholastic, 1987.
Hughes, Shirley. *When We Went to the Park*. Lothrop, Lee & Shepard, 1985.
Hutchins, Pat. *1 Hunter*. Greenwillow, 1982.
Mahy, Margaret. *When the King Rides By*. Ashton Scholastic, 1986.

Books to stimulate graphing topics:

Alexander, Anne. *ABC of Cars and Trucks*. Doubleday, 1971.
Anno, Mitsumasa. *Anno's Counting Book*. Harper & Row, 1977.
Bate, Lucy. *Little Rabbit's Loose Tooth*. Crown, 1975.
Hoban, Tana. *Is It Rough? Is It Smooth? Is It Shiny?* Greenwillow, 1984.
Kitamura, Satoshi. *When Sheep Cannot Sleep: The Counting Book*.
   Farrar, Straus & Giroux, 1986.
Slobodkina, Esphyr. *Caps for Sale*. HarperCollins, 1987.

Estimation

Bakken, Harold. *The Special String*. Prentice-Hall, 1981.
Barrett, Judi. *What's Left?* Atheneum, 1983.
Bester, Roger. *Guess What?* Crown, 1980.
Clement, Rod. *Counting on Frank*. Gareth Stevens, 1991.
Hennessey, B.G. *The Dinosaur Who Lived in My Backyard*. Viking, 1988.
Hines, Anna Grossnickle. *Maybe a Bandaid Will Help*. Dutton, 1984.
Lobel, Arnold. *On Market Street*. Greenwillow, 1981.
Maestro, Betsy. *The Guessing Game*. Grosset, 1983.
Titherington, Jeanne, *Pumpkin, Pumpkin*. Greenwillow, 1986.
Williams, Vera B. *A Chair for My Mother*. Greenwillow, 1982.

Time

Anno, Mitsumasa. *All in a Day.* Philomel, 1986.

Aylesworth, Jim. *The Completed Hickory Dickory Dock*, Atheneum, 1991.

Bowers, Kathleen. *At This Very Minute*. Little, Brown and Company, 1983.

Brook, Judy. *Around the Clock.* The Windmill Press, 1980.

Carle, Eric. *The Grouchy Ladybug.* T.Y. Crowell, 1977.

Corey, Dorothy. *Will It Ever Be My Birthday?* Albert Whitman, 1986.

de Regniers, Beatrice Schenk. *Waiting for Mama.* Clarion, 1984.

Gerstein, Mordicai. *The Sun's Day.* HarperCollins, 1989.

Gibbons, Gail. *Clocks and How They Go.* T.Y. Crowell, 1979.

Gordon, Sharon. *Tick Tock Clock.* Troll Associates, 1982.

Grossman, Bill. *The Guy Who Was Five Minutes Late.* HarperCollins, 1991.

Hawkins, Colin. *What Time Is It, Mr. Wolf?* Putnam, 1983.

Hutchins, Pat. *Clocks and More Clocks.* Macmillan, 1973.

Katz, Bobbi. *Tick-tock, Let's Read the Clock.* Random House, 1988.

Killingbrook, Julia. *What Time Is It, Mrs. Bear?* Morrow, 1985.

Llewelyn, Claire. *My First Book of Time.* Dorling Kindersley, 1992.

McMillan, Bruce. *Time to . . . .* Lothrop, Lee & Shepard, 1989.

Maestro, Betsy. *Around the Clock With Harriet.* Crown, 1984.

Mendoza, George. *The Scarecrow Clock.* Holt, Rinehart and Winston, 1971.

Pluckrose, Henry. *Time.* Watts, 1988.

Thompson, Carol. *Time.* Delacorte, 1990.

Warren, Cathy. *The Ten-Alarm Camp-Out.* Lothrop, Lee & Shepard, 1983.

Measurement

Adams, Pam. *Ten Beads Tall*. Child's Play, 1989.

Allington, Richard and Kathleen Krull. *Measuring*. Raintree, 1985.

Arnold, Caroline. *Measurements: Fun, Facts, and Activities*. Watts, 1984.

Branley, Franklyn. *How Little, How Much: A Book About Scales*. T.Y. Crowell, 1976.

Caple, Kathy. *The Biggest Nose*. Houghton Mifflin, 1985.

Fey, J.T. *Long, Short, High, Low, Thin, Wide*. T.Y. Crowell, 1971.

Hoban, Tana. *Is It Larger? Is It Smaller?* Greenwillow, 1985.

Johnston, Tony. *Farmer Mack Measures His Pig*. Harper & Row, 1986.

Kellogg, Steven. *Much Bigger Than Martin*. Dial, 1976.

Lionni, Leo. *Inch by Inch*. Scholastic, 1960.

Mahy, Margaret. *Jam*. Little, Brown, 1986.

Milhous, Katherine and Alice Dalgliesh. *The Turnip: An Old Russian Folk Tale*, Putnam, 1990.

Morimoto, Junko. *The Inch Boy*. Puffin, 1988.

Most, Bernard. *The Littlest Dinosaurs*. Harcourt Brace Jovanovich, 1989.

Myller, Rolf. *How Big Is a Foot?* Macmillan, 1972.

Nelson, JoAnne. *How Tall Are You?* Modern Curriculum Press, 1990.

Nesbit, E. *Melisande*. Harcourt Brace Jovanovich, 1989.

Money

Arnold, Caroline. *What Will We Buy?* Watts, 1983.
Asch, Frank. *Good Lemonade*. Watts, 1976.
Berenstain, Jan and Stan. *The Trouble With Money*. Random House, 1983.
Field, Rachel. *General Store*. Little, Brown and Co. 1988.
Gretz, Susanna. *Teddybears Go Shopping*. Macmillan, 1982.
Heide, Florence. *Treehorn's Treasure*. Holiday House, 1981.
Hoban, Lillian. *Arthur's Funny Money*. HarperCollins, 1981.
Hoban, Russell. *A Bargain for Frances*. Harper & Row, 1970.
Hoban, Tana. *26 Letters & 99 Cents*. Greenwillow, 1987.
Maestro, Betsy and Giulio. *Dollars and Cents for Harriet*. Crown, 1988.
Mathis, Sharon. *The Hundred Penny Box*, Viking Penguin, 1975.
Nelson, JoAnne. *The Magic Money Machine*. Modern Curriculum Press, 1990.
Pearson, Tracey. *The Storekeeper*. Puffin Books, 1991.
Rockwell, Anne. *Our Garage Sale*. Greenwillow, 1984.
Schwartz, David. *If You Made a Million*. Lothrop, Lee & Shepard, 1990.
Silverstein, Shel. "Smart" in *Where the Sidewalk Ends*. Harper & Row, 1970.
Vincent, Gabrielle. *Bravo, Ernest and Celestine!* Greenwillow, 1982.
Viorst, Judith. *Alexander, Who Used to Be Rich Last Sunday*. Atheneum, 1978.
Williams, Vera B. *A Chair for My Mother*. Greenwillow, 1982.
———. *Something Special for Me*. Greenwillow, 1983.

Fractions

Comber, B. *Dad's Diet*. Ashton Scholastic. 1987.
Dennis, J. Richard. *Fractions Are Parts of Things*. T.Y. Crowell, 1971.
Greenaway, Kate. *A-Apple Pie*. Castle Books, 1979.
Hughes, Shirley. *Lucy and Tom's 1, 2, 3*. Penguin, 1987.
Hutchins, Pat. *The Doorbell Rang*. Greenwillow, 1986.
Kellogg, Steven. *Johnny Appleseed*. Morrow Jr. Books, 1988.
Kuskin, Karla. *The Philharmonic Gets Dressed*. HarperCollins, 1982.
Lionni, Leo. *Pezzettino*. Pantheon, 1975.
Mathews, Louise. *Gator Pie*. Dodd, 1979.
McMillan, Bruce. *Eating Fractions*. Scholastic, 1991.
Nelson, J. *Half and Half*. Modern Curriculum Press, 1990.
Pomerantz, Charlotte. *The Half-Birthday Party*. Houghton Mifflin, 1984.

Notes

Notes